The Man Who Sent the SOS

Paul Amirault

Bear Notch Road Press

WEST HOLLYWOOD, CA

Printed in the United States of America

First Printing, 2017

Bear Notch Road Press
8424 Santa Monica Blvd. #A171
West Hollywood, CA 90069

Cover Art by Shealyn Thomson
Jack Phillips photo courtesy of the National Archives, UK
Book Layout © 2014 BookDesignTemplates.com

ISBN 978-0-9975704-0-3
eISBN 978-0-9975704-1-0

For Carol J. Amirault
1939-2014
Words will never be enough....

The curious sense of the whole thing being a dream was very prominent: that all were looking on at the scene from a near-by vantage point in a position of perfect safety, and that those who walked the decks or tied one another's lifebelts on were actors in a scene of which we were but spectators: that the dream would end soon and we should wake up to find the scene had vanished. Many people have had a similar experience in times of danger, but it was very noticeable on the Titanic's deck. I remember observing it particularly while tying on a lifebelt for a man on the deck. It is fortunate that it should be so: to be able to survey such a scene dispassionately is a wonderful aid in the destruction of the fears that go with it.

— LAWRENCE BEESLEY
Survivor and author, *The Loss of the S.S. Titanic: Its Story and Its Lessons*, 1912

CONTENTS

The Man Who Sent the SOS

A Note from the Author

I never thought I'd end up writing a "spiritual" book. When I was in my early twenties, after falling away from the church of my youth, I prided myself on my practicality. I extolled the virtues of reason, intellect, and common sense to anyone who'd listen—and especially to those up for indulging in that old taboo, *the religion argument.*

Since I always came to these scuffles well armed—and could quote and dissect Bible verses like the best of them—it pleased me when my opponents retreated into a corner. It also pleased me when, as a last-ditch effort, they invoked the "faith card," as if that somehow trumped—and ended—the debate.

And my childhood branch of Christianity wasn't the only religion that found its way into my crosshairs. I was always fascinated by belief systems in general, and therefore, spent a great deal of time researching many different faiths. I was trying to get a handle on what adherents believed—in an effort to possibly understand the origin of those beliefs.

So you can imagine my surprise when "the guy who thought he knew everything" was ultimately confronted by something he couldn't easily explain. It forced me to reexamine my views—and to embark on a 12-year quest to get to the bottom of the mystery. This book is the result.

You'll be reading all about it shortly, but first, please afford me a few moments to discuss some housekeeping details about my approach.

My goal was to chronicle everything as accurately as possible. The "Paul" chapters are memoir—presented in novelistic format. As a result, I've recreated conversations, meetings, and hypnosis sessions, based on memories, notes and journal entries, as well as the recollections of family members and friends. In certain instances—in order to protect the privacy of the people involved—I've changed names, locations or other identifying details; however, these alterations are clearly marked.

The "Jack" chapters are based on "memories," too—albeit of a somewhat different sort. You should know that, while I was writing, I didn't intentionally research things upfront. The images, words and details flowed to me, both during past-life regressions, and also as I banged away on my laptop, and it was only later that I took to the web to see if I could confirm the things I was seeing. The fact that this book exists at all is proof of—to my mind at least—the uncanny accuracy of the information.

But I'll let you be the judge of that.

And finally, let me say thank you, in advance, for allowing me to share my spiritual journey with you.

CHAPTER ONE

SKINNY DIPPING IN THE DARK

Paul, Norton, Massachusetts, August 1975

I was expecting it, and as soon as the sun dipped behind the trees, I got it.

"Why don't you take your shirt off now?" one of the Thompson[1] kids asked. "It's *night.*"

Busted. I was 12 years old, the fat kid, who always wore a T-shirt while swimming in our backyard pool. My excuse was I had sensitive skin and didn't want a sunburn, but obviously, this wasn't going to fly now.

Pretending not to hear, I quickly dove under, skimming porpoise-like along the bottom. What I needed was more time for the twilight to deepen into full-on night. It wasn't my rolls of fat I was ashamed of—it was my (what would later be

---

[1] Name has been changed to protect "the innocent."

called) man boobs—which had recently appeared, like alien sprouts, on my chest.

When I resurfaced, the question was repeated, and I had no choice but to respond with a vague "oh, yeah" and remove the shirt, which I tossed in a heap at the water's edge. Carefully keeping my chest submerged, I watched and waited as the darkness deepened. And just when I began to relax, my sister suddenly had the bright idea of turning on the lights.

The pool had two; one was a glowing orb submerged at the deep end, the other a floodlight attached to the rear of our house. Instinctively, I moved to the no-man's land halfway between the two lights to await the onslaught. Soon enough, it was bright as day in the pool area again. I was trapped.

Noticing my fingers were beginning to prune, I assumed we'd be getting out shortly. I already had an exit strategy: scurry after the last one and lunge for my towel. But unfortunately, no one seemed eager for the pool party to end. Especially now that it was just us kids.

The cookout had wrapped up hours earlier, and the adults—my parents and Mr. and Mrs. Thompson—had retreated to the house. Through the window beneath the floodlights, I could see them sitting around the kitchen table, laughing and playing cards. Just like our family, the Thompsons had five children, and since they lined up in ages with my siblings and me almost exactly, we all became great childhood friends.

We weren't exactly angels...at least us boys. We got into the kind of trouble kids growing up in the country often did: throwing crab apples or snowballs at moving cars; telling horrific (and mostly made-up) ghost stories to scare our younger sibs (with bonus points for making them cry); or passing around a beer lifted from our parents' cooler while dutifully pretending to like the taste.

However, on this muggy summer night, beer wasn't on tap...something even more memorable was. It began when one of the Thompsons asked, "Hey! You wanna go skinny dipping?"

There was a moment of stunned silence. The Thompsons were incredulous to learn my siblings and I had never done it. "Oh, you gotta try it," they said. "You won't believe how it feels!"

I was doubtful, but when my siblings began expressing interest, I saw an opportunity.

"We should probably turn off the lights," I said, gesturing toward the house. "Don't want them catching us...."

Agreeing this was a good call, my younger sister Laura— who'd barely toweled off—was soon sneaking back inside to surreptitiously extinguish the lights. Since the pool switch was farther away, it was flipped first.

When the light winked out, I was treading water, wondering if I'd actually have the nerve to remove my bathing suit. Frankly, I was feeling naked enough minus the T-shirt.

By chance, my eyes were drawn to the floodlight at the moment it clicked off. I was temporarily blinded. As my pupils struggled to adjust to the darkness, something terrifying appeared in my field of vision.

It was a gigantic ship—a huge wall of black steel that loomed ominously over my head. The vessel was completely dark—like a ghost ship.

For a split second, I had no idea where I was or what had happened. But then, physical sensation returned, and I gasped and literally ducked my head, as a wave of chills and goose-flesh swept over my body.

At that moment, there was a huge splash—one of the Thompsons had cannonballed into the water beside me, filling my gaping mouth and stinging my eyes.

I closed my eyes to flush away the chlorine, and when I reopened them, the eerie apparition had vanished.

"Obviously, there's no ship in my backyard," I told myself forcefully. "It must have been some trick of the light." Although the explanation satisfied my mind, it did nothing to calm my still-tingling flesh.

But now, however, I had other things to worry about. The Thompsons began cajoling me to remove my bathing suit. It took a great deal of prodding, but I eventually caved in, slipping off my trunks and tossing them in a heap atop my T-shirt. And that amazing free-floating feeling of swimming in the buff diverted my attention. The water was warm. It felt perfect.

Thus, it was relatively easy to focus on the fun I was having, and put that strange, ghostly vision out of my mind.

. . .

They say kids have a natural propensity for "moving on" quickly, and that was definitely the case with me. By the time school started again, the memory of the incident had begun to fade, covered over by new experiences—layer by layer—like pages in a scrapbook.

And I'm fairly certain I would've completely forgotten about it, too—if it weren't for the fact that, many years later, I ended up seeing that same "ghost ship" image again.

But this time, it was in such stunning detail, I could actually make out the rivets.

SPARKS

Jack, North Atlantic, April 15, 1912

The first thing Jack noticed when he got outside: his exhales were exploding in the night air like ragged puffs of smoke.

He pulled up the collar of his woolen overcoat, dug his hands in his pockets, and began making his way forward to the deck's end, where a crowd of passengers had gathered.

"Excuse me, excuse me," he said, pushing his way through the throng. When he got to the wooden railing, he saw an unimaginable sight: the bow of the ship was nearly submerged.

Black water sloshed around the base of the forward mast, which now resembled a tree trunk inundated by a river flood.

Jack sighed fiercely. Beyond the bow, the North Star was shining brightly. But that wasn't what drew his attention. On the horizon, the lights of a distant steamer bobbed merrily…a ship that, infuriatingly, hadn't responded to any of Jack's distress messages. He knew that another vessel was, at that very moment, racing through the night to reach them, but it was clear she would arrive too late.

Once again, Jack felt the bile rising in his throat.

There was loud shouting from behind, and he turned to see three teenagers pushing their way to the railing. They were Italians, by the look—and sound—of them. One of the boys jostled Jack as he passed, jabbering excitedly at the sight of the sunken bow.

Jack turned and made his way back to the hatchway.

"Anything?" he asked as soon as he entered the Marconi Room. His assistant Harold, a thin boy with an unruly shock of thick hair, shook his head.

"Made contact with the *Baltic* but she's too far away."

Returning to his chair, Jack relieved him at the key.

"How—" Harold started to ask, but Jack cut him off wearily.

"The foredeck's awash," he told him. "She can't last much longer. You better put on some more clothes—and your lifebelt."

Slipping his headphones[2] over his ears, Jack continued keying out the distress message.

C-Q-D C-Q-D C-Q-D…

CQD was the International code for "Attention all Stations: Distress."

…D-E…

---

[2] In Jack's time, headphones/earphones were called "telephones." However, to avoid confusion, I've opted to go with the current vernacular.

DE, in the parlance of wireless operators, stood for "from"

...M-G-Y M-G-Y M-G-Y.

MGY were the call letters for the ship: the *RMS Titanic*.

As the minutes crawled by, Jack was dimly aware that Harold was again hovering behind him. The boy had put his overcoat and lifebelt on, and was standing there with Jack's lifebelt in his hands. Knowing it would be impossible to slip the vest over Jack's head while he was wired to the headphones, Harold finally gave up. He placed the vest on the back of Jack's chair.

At that moment, the ship's captain poked his head into the cabin. "Abandon your post, men," he said.

Jack looked up from the Marconigraph. "Sir?"

"You can do no more," the old man said, looking at his hands. "So I release you from your duties."

The captain's face was ashen and his eyes puffy. It looked like he was fighting back tears. "You'll want to get on deck then," he said. "and look after yourselves."

"But, sir—" Jack stammered.

"That's the way of it, at times like these," the old man said as he left the room.

Jack paused for a moment, then turned back to the Marconigraph.

C-Q-D C-Q-D C-Q-D

As he resumed transmitting, a loud, ripping sound emanated from below, followed by a small jolt, which prodded Harold into action.

"I'll get our things," the boy said, hurrying off to the adjoining bedroom.

Jack didn't answer. He was concentrating on the wireless key, focusing his attention solely on the zap of electric spark that occurred with each stroke of his key.

M-G-Y M-G-Y M-G-Y

Suddenly, Harold was yelling, "Get off, get off!"

Jack turned with a start to see a strange crewman just inches from him. The man, a stoker or coal trimmer, was one of Titanic's many below-deck workers. Tall and lanky, his face and clothes were covered with a mixture of coal dust and sweat.

Jack stared at the boy, who had striking blue eyes and dirty blond hair. He hardly looked older than a teenager.

"He's trying to steal your lifebelt!" Harold shouted.

Jack gasped incredulously when he noticed that the boy's grimy hands were indeed clutching the lifebelt Harold had left on his chair.

In a flash, Jack threw down his headphones and jumped up, the chair toppling in the process. He lunged for the belt; however, the crewman refused to release it.

"Give it back!" Jack shrieked. But the stoker said nothing, his fingers merely tightening claw-like around the vest. Jack couldn't know that the boy had grown up in a Scandinavian country where the water was too cold for swimming, so he'd never learned—and thus considered Jack's lifebelt his only hope for survival.

Jack would've recognized the fear and desperation in the boy's eyes, had he been seeing clearly. But he was *not* seeing clearly. On the contrary, he was suddenly and completely filled with rage.

Seeing the look on Jack's face, Harold sprang into action. He lunged forward and grabbed the stoker from behind, pinning his arms to his side. But still, the boy refused to relinquish the vest.

Jack, his anger boiling over, began pummeling and pummeling him—until the stoker finally let go. Jack snatched back his vest and tossed it onto his worktable.

Since the boy was now grunting and writhing violently against Harold in an attempt to free himself, Jack exploded with righteous anger. He lashed out again and again, until his fist came in contact with the stoker's jaw. There was a loud crack, and Jack suddenly felt like his hand was on fire. Intense pain began shooting down his arm, too, but he was barely aware of it. He merely pounded harder—until the boy fell, slack-jawed and glassy-eyed, against Harold.

Although Jack wasn't aware of it, the "knock-out punch" wasn't solely the result of his fisticuffs; Harold, who'd been struggling to keep his balance on the tilting deck, had pushed the stoker forward at the precise moment Jack launched his final blow—catching the boy, between them, like a vice.

Now, however, Harold finally released his grip, and the stoker dropped to the faux-tile floor with a thud.

"He should've known where his own lifebelt was!" Harold exclaimed, once he was able to catch his breath.

Jack glanced at the stoker's motionless body for a moment, then turned his attention to the overturned chair. His hand shrieked in pain as he pulled it back upright. He reattached his headphones, and sat back down at the desk.

As he reached for the wireless key, Jack realized his index finger had broken. It was swollen, and he was unable to close it around the key. He pushed down anyway, and there was a zap of connection. He tried gripping the key a different way, but his hand continued to throb. It was useless.

Jack, defeated, took off his headphones and lowered his head to the table.

But soon there was another terrified shout from Harold.

"Jack, the water's coming!"

Jack nodded and slowly got up. He reached down and picked up his lifebelt, raising it over his head with difficulty.

"Can you give me a hand with this?" he asked, in a strangely calm voice.

Harold hurried over and quickly tied the belt's straps.

"I've got your money and your papers," he said.

"Put 'em in my pocket," Jack said. "Don't think I can do it."

Jack put his hand reflexively to his head and noticed his hat wasn't there. But he couldn't will himself to look for it.

"Let's go," he said, carefully stepping over the body of the stoker, who was still splayed out on the floor.

Jack and Harold met the flood of water halfway down the hall. As they splashed through the freezing liquid, it had a reinvigorating effect on Jack. But the going was now treacherous. They were forced to grip the side railing for support. Jack held on with his left hand only. His right hand was still in agony.

The ship was groaning all around them. Suddenly, there was a sharp jolt, accompanied by a terrifically loud crash from somewhere up front. The wheelhouse had apparently given way.

The hatchway up ahead now resembled a small waterfall.

"Dear God, please don't let her sink while we're in here," Jack implored as he and Harold quickened their pace.

"Please, God."

— — —

Approximately one hour and forty minutes later, the prayers of 705 men, women and children (mostly the latter two groups) were answered when the rescue ship Jack summoned arrived to pluck them from the icy water.

But a far greater number—some fifteen hundred people—weren't so lucky. They became victims of a shipwreck that, even today, remains one of the most haunting and notorious of all time.

Jack Phillips was among them.

He's considered by some to be a hero of the disaster. Others call him a villain, claiming he's at least partially responsible for the fate that befell the doomed liner.

Since Jack wasn't around to defend himself...and the stories told by those who did survive were conflicting (or, at the very least, "selectively" edited), it's widely assumed that the truth about what actually happened could never be known.

At one point in my life, I would've been of a similar opinion. But then, through an improbable set of circumstances, I stumbled upon the truth about Jack's story...and realized it was up to me to tell it.

CHAPTER THREE

THE REGRESSION

Paul, Sherman Oaks, California, Spring 1996

I couldn't help feeling kind of silly.

I was sitting in a darkened office, about to undergo a hypnotic past-life regression. The hypnotist, an attractive, smiling woman named Janeen Weiss, asked if I was comfortable.

Define *comfortable*.

I was an East Coast transplant who'd moved to Southern California nearly a decade earlier to pursue my dream of making movies. But the plan of becoming the next Steven Spielberg had quickly gone belly up—after I was forced to acknowledge a couple Hollywood truths: one, you have to eat; and two, there are far more paying jobs in television.

Since I enjoyed watching documentary-style programs, I didn't say no when a producer offered me an entry-level position to work on one. My job title was researcher. Right away, I discovered I had a knack for this line of work. I found it fun digging up information, talking to interesting people, and writing about the things I'd learned.

I eventually worked my way up to "Director of Research," which meant I supervised a small staff of researchers who were tasked with coming up with content for shows. And although I wasn't technically a *producer*—my team's research files were eventually turned over to more senior people—I had little to complain about. I was 33, a former small-town boy who was making a decent living in one of the world's toughest businesses, and overall, I was grateful.

But even so, the show I was working on at that moment—*Put to the Test*—was particularly stressful.

Its premise was straightforward. We took people's claims of paranormal phenomenon and/or abilities and tested them. For instance, if someone said, "I can speak to the dead," or "I have a ghost in my house," or "I can locate underground sources of water with my divining rod," we'd say, "That's great, that's wonderful, but if you don't mind, we'd like you to *prove it....*"

As you can imagine, it was a difficult show to book. Claimants of the paranormal don't exactly grow on trees—at least, the relatively sane ones—and most of those we did find (many of whom were already household names) balked at the program's skeptical nature. Their attitude was, "I'm famous for doing what I do, so why should I have to prove anything to *you*?"

Of course, they were right. The potential benefit of the national publicity we were offering (on the ABC Network) was more than offset by the potential embarrassment of failing our "test" in such a public forum.

Consequently, many subjects we approached declined to participate. And each pass was like a dagger to my heart, since production was scheduled to begin shortly, and we hadn't locked in all of our stories.

My boss, the show's Executive Producer, had even called an emergency meeting to vent his frustration over our lack of progress.

After spending a couple minutes glancing at our "Story Board"—which consisted of dozens of handwritten index cards—the E.P. said, "What about reincarnation?"

Several of the researchers responded, "Yeah, reincarnation, that's a good one." But I wasn't convinced.

As a life-long reader, I'd been exposed to the subject back in high school, after devouring the popular novels *Audrey Rose* and *The Reincarnation of Peter Proud.* And although the "romantic notion" of reincarnation interested me on a personal level, I didn't think it was something that could be actually proven.

One of the reasons I felt this way was because I'd already spent a great deal of time researching the subject. A few years earlier, when I was working on another paranormal show called *encounters: the hidden truth,* I'd learned of a school of thought that claimed ordinary people could be "hypnotized" to remember their past lives.

From what I understood, this form of hypnotic regression had come about as a by-product of ordinary hypnotic regression—a controversial psychiatric technique used by Freud and others to allow patients to relive their earliest memories. For example, a person could be brought back in time to talk about things he or she had experienced as a child. Therapists apparently found this technique useful in helping their patients remember blocked memories of traumatic events.

The "past-life" part came about when patients—or their hypnotists—went too far, and the regressed subject started talking about things they'd supposedly experienced in a previous lifetime. In the 1950s, a Colorado housewife named Virginia Tighe underwent hypnosis and described the life of a 19th-century Irish woman named Bridey Murphy. The details Tighe revealed while in trance were investigated, and—in at least a couple of instances—found to have checked out. For instance, the local Belfast grocery stores where "Bridey" claimed to have shopped had once existed, but had been out of business for more than fifty years.

Despite such impressive hits, however, the "Bridey Murphy" case, to my mind, illustrated the main flaw with the idea that reincarnation and/or past-life regression could be tested in any meaningful way. If the information about a supposed "past life" existed for the purpose of validation, how could it be proven the "regressed" person hadn't been inadvertently exposed to it beforehand...or worse, hadn't actually researched it up front?

And for the purposes of our TV show, there was another problem to consider: the amount of time required to corroborate a past-life story. As I knew well, Tighe's amateur hypnotist had spent almost a year investigating "Bridey's" tale—which was time we certainly didn't have...since the show had to be delivered in just a few months. (The network had already announced an airdate.)

Given these problems, I thought the subject would be a waste of time to pursue, and summoning up the nerve, I told this to the Executive Producer.

"Nice try," he said, before ordering me to research the subject.

Going back to my office, I dug through my Rolodex and found the home phone number for Janeen Weiss, a woman whom I'd worked with on a talk-show pilot a couple of years before.

I remembered Janeen had recently sent me a card announcing she'd become a past-life hypnotherapist. At the time I'd thought, hey, novel career change, but who was I to criticize? Janeen had been fun to work with, and she always seemed quite levelheaded. She wasn't someone I'd consider a "wacko" in the least.

I gave her a call and we talked for almost an hour. Janeen's views on past-life regression were interesting. She said it was frankly amazing the diverse stories people came up with while under hypnosis—especially those with phobias or other unusual obsessions. For example, someone deathly afraid of flying would often talk about dying in a plane crash in a past life. In many of these cases, according to Janeen, simply talking about the experience gave the person insight into their phobia and cured them. And whether these stories were real—or dream-like fabrications of the subconscious mind—was beside the point.

"I tend to take a practical view of the matter," she said. "Who cares if it's real, as long as it works? And for some strange reason, past-life regression hypnotherapy does work. It really does."

For the record, Janeen wasn't in the reincarnation camp. She believed patients' past-life stories were probably mind creations. But one thing she was certain of: anyone could be regressed to his or her "past lives."

"Even you, Paul," she said matter-of-factly. Although she shared my belief the subject wasn't testable per se, she offered me a free session so I could see for myself what hypnotic past-life regression was like. I took her up on it right away. I figured it couldn't hurt—it would actually be kind of fun—and at least I'd get out of the office for a little while.

However, I knew I wouldn't be able to devote a lot of time to this "field trip." I had the sneaking suspicion that—despite the Executive Producer's opinion—reincarnation via past-life regression wouldn't prove suitable for *Put to the Test*, and, in the end, it would still be my job to find produce-able stories for the show.

Thus, when the day of my regression came, I was focused on finding substitute claimants. Given my preoccupation, I was glad that, shortly after arriving at Janeen's office, she got down to business right away.

She closed the drapes and sat me in an overstuffed armchair. I took out the mini-tape recorder I'd brought—being the perennial Boy Scout, I knew it never hurt to be prepared. Pressing the record button, I placed it on the table next to me, as Janeen took a seat a couple feet away.

She took me through the process. First, she'd hypnotize me with a series of relaxation exercises. Then, when I was fully "under," the actual regression would begin.

I was disappointed to learn the induction wouldn't include having me watch a swinging pendulum. Janeen explained this was just a Hollywood cliché and not the most effective way of inducing trance. Her technique required only listening to her voice.

I don't recall much of the induction. I just remember hearing her flat monotone, which had an almost musical cadence. She was saying things like, "Your arms are getting heavier. Feel how heavy your arms are. See how good it feels to relax," etc. Naturally, I began to relax.

I remember thinking that, pretty soon, I'd be so relaxed I'd fall asleep and start snoring. However, as comfortable as my body was becoming, my mind remained alert. I was completely aware of where I was...and what I was doing. I didn't know what being hypnotized was supposed to "feel like," but I was pretty sure what I was feeling at that moment wasn't it.

When Janeen started telling me to go back, way back in my mind to a time before I was born, I panicked and spoke up: "But I'm not under yet."

Janeen paused for a moment. "Yes, you are," she said. Then, in that same pleasant voice, she asked me to try and lift my arm. I tried my hardest, but it felt as if my hand had been glued to the chair.

"You're hypnotized, all right," she said, matter-of-factly. Then she began again, asking my mind to go back to a time when I had lived before. I remember being disappointed she hadn't tried to ease the passage by regressing me to memories of my own childhood first. But perhaps, I thought, since this was a freebie, I wouldn't be getting all the bells and whistles.

I realized I should try to focus. How could I expect results if I was wisecracking the entire time? I tried to put distracting thoughts out of my head and concentrate on what she was saying.

But unfortunately, it didn't help. The only thing that "came to me" was the sound of the wall clock, the whir of my mini-recorder, and the distant rumble of traffic on Ventura Boulevard. To her credit, though, Janeen kept at it for several minutes; however, my mind—hypnotized or not— refused to cooperate.

Finally, she changed her approach. "Sometimes," she said in that patient voice, "a person has physical marks on their body that connect in some way to a past-life experience. Think about your body," she said. "Think about any imperfections you have...think about your birthmarks. If you have any scars, think about them."

"What about the big gut hanging over my belt?" I thought darkly. "Will that work?" I decided not to go there. I had no interest in learning I'd been Henry the 8th in a past life.

Trying to silence the annoying play-by-play in my mind, I began to picture my body. At one point, I started thinking about my right calf. A few years earlier, I'd developed a large wine-colored scar there. When it first appeared, I'd gone to the doctor in alarm. But the doc assured me it wasn't life threatening. Apparently, a blood vessel in my leg had ruptured, staining the underside of my skin in the process. The doctor told me my varicose veins had caused the rupture. As he well knew, I'd been afflicted by this old lady disease—particularly on the inside of my right calf—since I was a teen.

Figuring this was as good a bodily imperfection as I'd be able to come up with, I began to picture, in my mind's eye, my wine-stained calf, hidden—as it was—beneath my khaki pants.

Then something weird happened.

Suddenly, I was somewhere else.

I was outside, in terrifically bright sunshine.

I was on the beach—or more accurately—I was running through shallow water just off the beach of what looked like a tropical island. But I wasn't running along the beach…I was running out to sea.

It was obviously some sort of a bay or harbor—I could see a landmass to my right protruding into the ocean. The water was a brilliant blue, and the sand beneath my feet an unnatural white. Although I sensed I was several yards from shore, the water remained shallow.

Looking around, I saw there were others alongside me; people who—like me—were also running away from the shore. I couldn't help but notice these people were brown-skinned and wearing minimal "native" clothing. I held up my own arm and looked at it. It was bony and very brown.

"Wow," I thought, "this is weird!"

I saw the others and I were making for boats that were scrambling to the open ocean. The boats—a type of out-rigger canoe—were already partially occupied. I grabbed a hold of one and began to run with it.

At that moment, I became aware that other "natives" in the water were following us. Correct that—were *chasing us!*

Too late, I turned, and found that one of these natives was bearing down upon me. This unknown person raised a spear, and in a flash, I felt it bury itself on the inside of my right calf. I doubled over in pain, falling down into the knee-deep water. I was dimly aware that the canoe I'd been attempting to push along was continuing out to sea.

I was abandoned—and surrounded by enemies.

Then, just as quickly as it had come, the scene vanished. I was back, sitting in Janeen's darkened office.

She asked me to describe what I'd seen, but I struggled to find the words. I was struck by how quick—and matter-of-fact—it had all been. Despite the violent act I had just witnessed, I didn't have a strong emotional attachment to the experience. I had merely watched it, clinically, as if I'd been watching a movie.

Janeen asked if I wanted to return to that particular life to experience more of it. I shook my head. Looking back, it's possible I hadn't actually wanted to learn what happened next. Given that my attacker could just as easily have speared me through the heart, it's possible that wounding—at least temporarily—had been his main objective. What subsequent horrors were inflicted upon this luckless native, I didn't—and *still don't*—want to guess.

For some reason, though, I found myself saying, "No, there's something else."

Janeen was quiet for a moment, and then she said, "Okay, apparently your subconscious has something it wants to show you. I want you to relax…just go with it…and allow your mind to show you what it needs for you to see."

Her words had barely died out when I was somewhere else. Again.

I was in the water, but this time, it was night.

Looking up, I saw a towering wall of black steel looming over me. I was less than ten feet from a large ship—so close I could see its glistening portholes and rivets clearly. No light shone from inside the vessel. It was a dark, hulking mass.

Oddly, the mental picture came without accompanying physical sensations of any kind. Even the sound appeared to have been switched off. The only thing I could hear was my own breathing, which began to quicken reflexively. And unlike the cool detachment with which I'd experienced the previous "life," this image filled me with such dread and horror that I ended up snapping out of the regression completely. (Or at least, that's how it felt at the time. Janeen told me later she'd seen my distress and immediately brought me back to waking consciousness. But I remembered none of it.)

My eyes flew open.

As I tried to shake the hypnotically induced torpor from my limbs, I kept replaying the image in my mind.

From the second I'd seen the ship, I'd recognized it immediately: the *RMS Titanic*.

I'd been obsessed by the story of the tragic White Star liner for many years, and although I knew the vessel by sight, my certainty at that moment came less from the visuals, and more from a deeper, gut-level sense of *knowing*.

. . .

Titanic's woeful tale had taken root in my consciousness back when I was seven-years old. My second-grade teacher, Mrs. Thorpe, had spent several weeks reading to the class Walter Lord's book, *A Night to Remember*, which recounted the events on the night the ship sank. I remember being shocked and amazed by the story. Each day, I couldn't wait to get to her classroom to hear more of it.

When I was ten or eleven, I first experienced the feeling of being "blown away" by a movie. The film was the original 1950s *Titanic* (starring Clifton Webb and Barbara Stanwyck), which came on TV one Sunday afternoon. (I watched it with my dad.) The final shot of the movie...where the lifeboats are seen in the foreground as the ship quietly sinks in the background...literally gave me the shivers.

Shortly thereafter, my dad gave me his old 8mm movie camera, and one of my first cinematic endeavors was to try and recreate that haunting image. But unfortunately, Cecil B. DeMille I wasn't. A neighbor's old rowboat (piloted by my brother and a friend) stood in for the *Titanic* lifeboat; the weed-choked pond at the end of our street became the Atlantic Ocean; and, to recreate the sinking ship, I upended a model battleship and filmed it in a bathtub. Then, using rudimentary special-effect techniques, I was able to combine the two images—although the results weren't pretty—and I realized special effects might not be my forte.

However, despite the film's lackluster response, my enthusiasm for the ship remained undiminished, although it wasn't until the wreck was actually found that I got my first clue that my fascination with *Titanic* went beyond the ordinary.

In September of 1985, I was working as a waiter at a Boston restaurant. Earlier that summer, I'd moved to Beantown from the small Massachusetts town where I'd grown up. Having just graduated from college with a degree in film production, I was naturally broke, and needed a day job to keep me afloat while I pursued my dream career.

On the day Robert Ballard and company located the wreck, I was standing at the bar waiting to pick up a drink order for one of my tables.

Words from the TV suddenly intruded on my thoughts—a promo for an upcoming news story.

"Navy scientists discover the remains of a legendary shipwreck...."

Looking up at the TV, I saw the words "*Titanic Found!*" superimposed over a grainy, black-and-white photo of the wreck.

For reasons I didn't understand, I began to cry. Not just a tear or two, but a torrent.

And these weren't tears of joy. I'm not the kind of guy who cries when he's happy. Crying was something I only did at funerals—and fortunately, I'd only been to one or two of those in my life at that time.

And yet there I was, sobbing like a baby. This was seriously weird. And worse—seriously embarrassing!

I quickly left the bar and went into the kitchen to be alone. I remember leaning against a counter, trying to pull myself together. A waitress came in with a tray of dirty dishes.

"Are you O.K.?" she asked.

"Yeah," I said, "Just got something in my eye."

She suggested I go to the sink and wash it out.

Figuring cold water on my face would do me a world of good, I took her advice. It did. Soon I was okay enough to get back to work—with my fragile male ego intact.

My strange crying episode, however, only deepened my fascination with all things *Titanic*. In 1987, when scientists from Ballard's most recent expedition to the wreck gave a lecture at Massachusetts Institute of Technology, I naturally had to go. I was thrilled when I saw they'd brought with them Jason Jr. (JJ), the floating robotic camera that had taken all those amazing photos for *National Geographic* magazine.

After the lecture, I went on stage to get a closer look at JJ. I noticed the small blue robot rested on twin stubby skis, the tips of which protruded from the front like a snowmobile's. I got a lump in my throat when I realized that JJ's skis had actually set down on *Titanic*'s deck.

When no one was looking, I reached down and ran a finger along the underside of one of the skis. I felt an electric thrill knowing I had touched something that had touched *Titanic*.

Looking back on this incident, I had to admit that I was a serious *Titanic* geek. But had my passion for the subject caused my subconscious mind to conjure up the sinking ship image during the "regression?" Or was there some other explanation?

— — —

Getting up awkwardly from the armchair, I clicked off the tape recorder and dropped it into my gym bag.

"Are you okay?" Janeen asked.

I don't remember my answer, but I probably just nodded. I was on autopilot—my mind still whirring from everything I'd seen.

I thanked Janeen, and got ready to leave.

"Don't be surprised if you experience some post-hypnotic memories in the coming weeks," she said. "Sometimes, patients who've been regressed will have a spontaneous flashback to the life they glimpsed while under hypnosis."

I asked if this was common.

"Yes," she said, "because hypnosis tends to open up pathways in the brain that lead directly to the subconscious. Normally, your waking mind suppresses them, but now that you've been primed, the odds are higher that something might "trigger you and bring up more stuff."

As I left Janeen's office, the bright sunshine on the street was a shock to my senses. I remember getting into my car and collapsing in the seat.

"What the hell just happened?" I thought. I felt like I'd been run over by a truck.

CHAPTER FOUR

NIGHT TERROR

Paul, Encino and West Hollywood, CA, 1996

By the time I got back to the office, I'd somewhat pulled myself together.

I went to see my friend Ruth Rivin right away, plopping down in a chair in front of her desk.

Although Ruth and I had been friends for many years, this wasn't a social call. Ruth had recently been promoted to Co-ordinating Producer of *Put to the Test*, and therefore she was eager to hear the details of my regression for work purposes.

"Well?" she asked.

"It was pretty awesome," I said, "I know it sounds crazy—but I think I saw the *Titanic*!"

After I shared with her my account—which she concurred had been "cool"—we began to talk about the practicality of testing the concept of reincarnation using my regression as a sample case.

Ruth pointed out that, since I hadn't actually come up with potentially verifiable details about either of my "past lives," a regression like mine—for the purposes of the show—would be a considered a failure.

The practical side of me realized she was right, despite the fact that I was still tripping, because I knew that it just wouldn't be possible to communicate the extreme vividness of the experience to a TV audience.

"Yeah," I said at last, "I think that's the problem with the whole concept. It really is a crapshoot. We could end up hypnotizing dozens of people...and still not get much more information than I got..."

Ruth nodded in agreement. She said she'd come around to my way of thinking (that reincarnation wouldn't work for the show). She promised to relay that information to the Executive Producer—since he hadn't wanted to hear it from me earlier.

I thanked her, and got ready to leave. "We'll keep digging," I said.

"I appreciate that," she responded.

Over the next several days, as my researchers and I continued struggling to identify replacement stories, I spent a great deal of time thinking about the regression. Was Janeen right? Had my subconscious mind created the native-getting-stabbed-in-the-leg scenario, as a way of explaining—and therefore helping my conscious mind deal with—the unsightly blood stain on my leg? It seemed far-fetched.

However, it was no more far-fetched than the opposite conclusion—that, in a past life, I'd been that native, and my current body had somehow created the bloodstain as a reminder of his injury.

On the other hand, the scene that played out in my head had been so realistic...and had come completely from left field. I had no affinity for—or even, *interest in*—Pacific Island cultures. With the exception of a brief work visit to Hawaii, I'd never been to a tropical island. In fact, the sum total of my experience on the subject of native islanders had come from watching the stereotypical denizens of *Gilligan's Island* and *King Kong*. Hell, I didn't even like going to the beach!

So, it was hard to believe I'd conjured it all up, given that the contents of this "life" were so alien to my current interests and experiences.

The ship image, on the other hand, was a different matter. Unlike the native bit, which had come about as a result of my thinking about my leg, this one had exploded out of nowhere. However, from a skeptical point of view, it was easier to explain, given my previously established fascination with *Titanic*. My mind could have served up the image as a way of validating this obsession.

But the converse could also be true; being a victim of the wreck of the *Titanic* in a previous life would certainly explain an interest in the ship and its doomed passengers in this one. It was like the old rhetorical question about the chicken and the egg. Which had come first?

And if—for the sake of argument—I were to assume that both images had indeed come from past-life experiences, I wondered why the native death scene—or near-death scene— had come to me in such an immersive, hyper-realistic way, while the *Titanic* image had seemed more surreal.

And the more I thought about it, I realized this wasn't the only difference between the two experiences. There'd also been my reaction. I'd perceived the "stabbing of the native" scenario with a sort emotional detachment, while the *Titanic* image had instantly filled me with dread. Of course, one possible explanation might be that the *Titanic* "life" was clearly the more recent of the two, given that the ship had sunk in 1912, and I was pretty sure there hadn't been any primitive island cultures in existence since that time.

But still, as I saw it, everything boiled down to one of three possibilities: both were past lives; neither were past lives; or one was and one wasn't. And I had no idea which of these was actually true.

One night, as I lay in bed replaying the image of that looming wall of black steel in my mind once again, I suddenly remembered that scary, ghost-like apparition from my backyard pool.

As I recalled details from that long ago summer night, I found myself shivering once again. I clearly remembered how I'd had to convince myself that the ship I'd seen had been some sort of optical illusion. But had it been?

In thinking about the particulars of the image—a low-angle view of the ship from its port side—I realized it was unique in the annals of Titanica, at least as far as artistic depictions of its sinking were concerned.

While I'd been fascinated by the sinking shot in the 1950's *Titanic* film, the view from water level was markedly different—so much so that I'd never previously made the connection between the *RMS Titanic* and the weird ship I'd seen that night in the pool.

Then something else occurred to me. No doubt part of the reason I'd found the sight of that looming wall of steel so disturbing—both as a teen, and later, during the regression—was because, for as long as I can remember, I'd been terrified of tall buildings. Funny enough, I wasn't afraid of being *inside* one. Heights didn't bother me. I could be hundreds of feet above the ground, leaning over the railing of some Observation Deck, and feel nothing but excitement at the breathtaking view.

Oddly, the difficulty occurred at street level—where I got completely and inexplicably "ooged out" every time I looked *up* at a skyscraper. (I eventually learned to mitigate the problem by intentionally looking down as I entered a high-rise— although bizarrely, I'd almost always duck my head as well.)

I knew this was an unusual personality quirk, but it begged the question of whether or not my subconscious mind had presented the towering wall of steel as a way of illustrating and explaining away this fear. Or, on the other hand, if the phobia had been created in a past life by having actually seen this. Once again, it was the chicken and the egg.

As I lay in bed pondering these imponderables, something else happened—and it was more terrifying than anything else I'd experienced to date.

One moment I was lying comfortably in my bed, trying to shut off my overactive brain and get some sleep, when suddenly, I saw myself on the deck of a ship, at night, hanging onto the railing for dear life as it plunged toward the water.

Looking forward, I could see the bow disappearing into the roiling black sea. I had the same sickening feeling I get on a roller coaster making a particularly steep plunge. The thing was really moving! I felt myself hitting the water, and going under. I could see the dark bubbles swirling around me. And still, I felt myself falling and falling, into the blackness.

My eyes flew open. It took several minutes for my heart to stop racing. Had I fallen asleep and actually been dreaming? I didn't think so. No dream had ever seemed so intense. Or was this one of those "spontaneous memories" Janeen had warned me about? If so, I hoped they wouldn't become a regular occurrence—because they could drive a guy insane!

I lay there thinking about what I'd just experienced. I didn't understand this "flashback," as it appeared to contradict the earlier image of *Titanic* that I'd seen. Looking at it logically, it made no sense. If, in a past life, I'd actually been a victim of the wreck, how could I have been in the water, just off the port side of the ship…and then go down with it as well?

Theoretically, I supposed, it would be possible for someone to be in the water alongside the ship, and then later, climb back aboard before the final plunge, but this scenario seemed a bit of a stretch.

And there was another oddity. *Titanic* had foundered with more than 1,500 people on board. And yet, in my vision, there was no one else in "my" immediate vicinity. Perhaps this was another clue that Janeen was right and what I was seeing wasn't real.

On the other hand, many of *Titanic*'s victims had reportedly gathered at the stern before the sinking, and—as everyone knows—it was a big ship. The person I'd seen in the "flashback" appeared to be smack dab in the middle of the vessel at the time of the plunge, so perhaps that could be explained as well.

However, as I lay in bed, tossing and turning, the thought that kept resurfacing, as the "flashback" continued to play and replay in my mind, was how real it had felt. The experience seemed every bit as vivid and life-like as the stabbing of the South Sea native had felt during the regression.

So perhaps both were bona fide past-life memories?

CHAPTER FIVE

SLAMMING DOORS

Jack, Farncombe, England, April 1902

Fifteen-year-old Jack lay in bed tossing and turning. He wasn't trying to sleep; he knew sleep wouldn't come now—at least until he got something to eat. But even if his stomach were full, he wasn't sure he'd be able to shut down his mind and rest. Too much had happened that day.

For starters, he'd been sent to bed without supper. Actually, that was the last thing that happened, and Jack had to admit it was a fitting capper to a wretched day. Although he'd been sent to bed without supper before—it typically happened after a fight with his father—there was nothing else typical about that evening.

Jack had never seen his father so mad. As the old man shouted at him, the prominent vein in his forehead had actually bulged.

Jack had predicted this, of course, which is why he'd stayed away from home until the last possible moment, arriving just as his mother was putting food on the table.

He'd spent much of the afternoon wandering around town—going first to the river to skip stones, and then to the Gas Works to see the giant gas tanks that had delighted him as a child.

Although it was now late April, the weather remained wintery and gray.

During his meandering journey, Jack dutifully toted his bundle of schoolbooks, which were bound by a leather strap. He briefly considered pitching the lot of them into the River Wey, but didn't dare. He knew throwing away his books would only make things worse. His parents—especially his father—would be furious enough he'd quit school.

That's right. He'd actually done it. Walked right out of Grammar School—in the middle of a lesson!

But Jack had never intended for his days as a scholar to end so abruptly. On the contrary, from his first day of school, he'd faithfully kept up with his studies, and he'd met some new friends, including his best mate, George, who helped make the experience relatively enjoyable.

However, at the start of the current school year, things changed. The old schoolmaster had retired, and Jack didn't like his replacement one bit.

The man—who had a long mustache and an even longer nose—was a bully. A tyrant, really. In addition to publicly ridiculing students if they made mistakes, the new schoolmaster often patrolled the classroom with his heavy wooden ruler raised and ready to rap the knuckles of anyone caught daydreaming during reading assignments. Jack, who regularly entertained thoughts of escaping the schoolhouse, had occasionally been on the receiving end of such blows.

"But not today," he thought, with unrepentant glee.

He'd been called upon to answer a question, and as he struggled for the answer, the schoolmaster began mocking him. His ears burned with embarrassment. Then, without thinking, he found himself calling the teacher a choice name in return. His classmates' titters were cut off with a gasp.

"Leave this classroom at once!" the schoolmaster bellowed.

But Jack was already on his feet, gathering his belongings, knocking aside pencils and a closed bottle of ink in the process.

As he stormed from the room, Jack could see the teacher's incredulous face. The man was obviously trying to process the fact that one of his students had dared to stand up to him.

After the classroom door had banged shut behind him, Jack's only regret was not having a chance to steal a look at George. He would've loved to have seen the expression on his friend's face at that moment. But he knew he'd hear about it later.

In the dim light of Jack's bedroom, however, his self-satisfied smile faded a bit, as his thoughts shifted, ultimately, to home and his parents' reaction.

"Oh, Jack, how could you?" his mother had said at last, while his older sister Ethel clucked disapprovingly.

Then his father piped in: "You're going to march back there tomorrow morning and apologize."

Jack was surprised. It hadn't occurred to him that this might be his father's reaction.

"I won't do it!" he said. "I'm not going back there."

"Go to your room and think about it, young man," his father said, trying to keep his anger in check.

"I won't change my mind!" Jack retorted, and instantly regretted it.

His father's anger boiled over. "You good-for-nothing brat!" he shouted. "Get out of my sight!"

Jack stalked off to his bedroom. He considered slamming his door, but didn't—at least not intentionally. However, it did close a bit loudly—with a dull thud that echoed throughout the apartment—and he knew there'd be trouble.

From the dining room, Jack could hear the murmur of hushed voices, followed by the scrape of his father's chair on the wooden floor. Then his old man's footfalls thundered down the hallway.

The door to his bedroom flew open, and the old man stood glowering at him.

"I didn't mean to slam it," Jack said.

Ignoring this, his father shouted, "You think you're too good for school?"

"No," Jack whispered finally.

"What was that?" his father roared.

"No, sir," Jack said, averting his eyes.

"Well, you're not gonna be a lay-about here," his father said. "Tomorrow, we're going to find you a job. It's time you earned your keep!"

The old man turned on his heels and stormed out, slamming the bedroom door behind him, shaking the entire room and causing the pictures on Jack's bureau to topple.

Jack's legs suddenly felt weak. He stumbled over to his bed, and the tears began flowing as soon as he hit the pillow.

"They can't make me," he said, over and over to himself. "I won't do it!"

As night fell and after he'd cried himself out, Jack began formulating a plan—not the least of which involved getting something to eat.

Now, hours later, his stomach flopped once again. He knew he'd have to make his move soon.

He was pretty sure the coast was clear. There'd been no sound from outside for a couple of hours.

Jack got up from bed, his stockinged feet tiptoeing across the hardwood floor. Opening his bedroom door carefully, he peered down the hall. To the left, his sister's bedroom door stood ajar. No doubt Ethel had left it open on purpose, so she could catch him if he attempted to raid the larder during the night.

Jack inched his way down the hallway and paused before Ethel's door. The sound of her fitful snoring could be heard.

He had a complicated relationship with his older sister. Ethel, along with her twin Elsie, had been thirteen when Jack was born. But while Elsie had left home shortly after finishing her studies (she was now a schoolmistress in a nearby town), Ethel had remained behind. She suffered from chronic health problems caused by a bout of meningitis when she was younger. However, this was rarely discussed in the Phillips household. The disease had also struck Jack's older brother Fred—who was just a baby—and the boy hadn't survived.

Jack occasionally felt bad for Ethel, who could be sweet and who, despite her illness, often helped their parents by sewing clothes and doing other light work around the house. But there was another side to Ethel that only Jack could see. He felt that, on some level, she was constantly competing with him for the love of their mother and the attention of their father.

Too often during his childhood, Jack thought, Ethel had played—with delight, it seemed to him—the role of family policeman, dutifully reporting any and all of his transgressions to their parents in order to curry favor.

Of course, Jack hadn't needed Ethel's help today; he'd done a fine job all by himself. However, as he broke his news, Ethel had looked at their parents, eyes wide in disbelief, her lips curled in a smug "I told you so" expression. Jack had had the urge to slap her.

He peered into Ethel's bedroom. She was obviously asleep.

Jack knew Ethel had a hard life, and he could only imagine what it was like for her to endure the occasional hospitalizations and day-to-day struggles brought about by her illness; however, in his heart of hearts, he just wished she were more like Elsie.

Elsie was not at all like her twin. She and Jack enjoyed a close relationship that was easy and uncomplicated. It had been Elsie (not his parents, nor Ethel) who relayed to Jack the story about the illness that had stricken Ethel and claimed the life of baby Fred.

Elsie and Jack enjoyed each other's company, and shared the same wicked sense of humor. Since Elsie had moved out while Jack was still a child, her visits—especially around the holidays—always seemed to be special times for Jack.

Another plus was that Ethel generally deferred to her twin, so Jack could usually count on a brief respite from her tattletales when Elsie was around.

Elsie's visits were always fun, especially when he was younger, whether she indulged him by letting him to jump up and down on her bed (Ethel never permitted such things), or by reading him stories or teaching him exotic games.

As he recalled Elsie's smiling face, Jack wondered what his older sister would think when she heard he'd quit school.

He knew Ethel would write her tomorrow—if she hadn't done so already, so he vowed to go to the post office the first thing in the morning and send his own letter. That way, Elsie would hear the news from him first.

Satisfied with his plan, Jack continued down the hall, simultaneously listening for Ethel's snoring, while also making sure not to step on any of the creaky floorboards, the locations of which he knew by heart.

When he got to the kitchen, which was at the rear of the apartment, he knew he'd have to be careful. His parents' bedroom was directly below, and he didn't want to cause any sudden noises that might wake them.

Before Jack was born, his parent's bedroom had been Jack's current one, while his sisters had shared the room next to it. The Phillips lived in a second floor apartment above the drapery store they managed. However, shortly after the arrival of Jack, in the spring of 1887, Jack's parents had been forced to move downstairs, converting an old storeroom behind the shop into a bedroom.

Jack had come to think his father resented him for that, too.

Bending over in the darkened kitchen, Jack quickly relieved the icebox of some slices of ham that had been left over from Sunday's dinner. He ate greedily—and soundlessly.

In many ways, he was at a crossroads, with boyhood behind him and manhood stretching out in front of him. He was about to make his way into the world. Many uncertainties lay before him, but he was sure of one thing: whatever happened in his life from this point forward would be of his own making. It was his life—not his parents', not his teacher's—and he had no intention of wasting a minute of it.

When he'd eaten his fill—or at least, as much as he dared—he headed off to bed.

The ham in his stomach allowed him to fall asleep quickly, and the next morning, he was up with the sun. After scratching out a letter to Elsie, Jack washed and put on his Sunday finest.

His parents were surprised to see him dressed, and even more surprised to hear he didn't want breakfast.

"So you've decided to go back to school then," his father said.

"No, sir," Jack said respectfully. "I've decided to apply for a job at the post office in town."

Jack figured his parents wouldn't be too shocked by the news—given how he'd been expressing his desire to become a telegraph operator for several years now. (Back in Jack's time, sending mail wasn't the only service provided by the post office. Telegrams could also be sent from there, for an additional fee.)

"I see," his father said finally, as he took his seat at the dining room table.

Thankfully, there was no further discussion, and Jack was able to escape the apartment. His mother walked him to the stairwell—wordlessly slipping a couple of pieces of bread into his hand.

Nibbling on his breakfast, Jack made the familiar walk into town. However, instead of going directly to the post office, he made a side trip to George's house, arriving just as his friend came out toting his bundle of schoolbooks.

"Thanks a lot, Jack," George said as soon as he saw him. "The schoolmaster gave us extra homework on account of you."

"Really?" Jack said. He honestly hadn't considered this.

"What did you think he would do?" George retorted, and began walking away.

"C'mon, George," Jack said, hurrying to catch up. "I didn't know—"

Without looking back, George cut him off.

"My parents said I shouldn't talk to you anymore," he said, continuing to march away. "They say you'll come to a bad end."

Jack considered catching up with him, but decided to let him go.

"The heck with you," he shouted after him, "and *your parents!*"

However, as he continued the long walk into town, Jack was at least prepared for the stony silence he encountered when he saw other classmates making their way to school.

"I'll show them," he thought, as the latest one ignored him. "I'll show them all."

His attention was now focused solely on the post office. He planned to do everything in his power to get a job. It was a matter of pride.

As it turned out, his letter to Elsie didn't get mailed that day. In his rush to leave the apartment, Jack had forgotten to bring money for postage, and as he walked home, he suffered knowing that Elsie would probably receive the news about him quitting school from Ethel first.

His fears turned out to be founded; Ethel's (no doubt) gossipy letter arrived a full day before his. However, when Jack did write Elsie again, a few weeks later, it was to share happier news: he was indeed hired by the post office, and although he was just a messenger boy, the opportunity for advancement existed. If he worked hard, the postmaster had told him, and received satisfactory grades on his Civil Service exam, he might become trained as a telegraph operator.

Jack ended the letter to Elsie by saying he planned on working very hard indeed!

. . .

The moment when Jack had first decided to pursue a career in telegraphy had taken place without fanfare of any sort. It had occurred in mid-summer, after his family had returned from a long-overdue holiday on the Isle of Wight. Jack had been eleven years old.

A few weeks earlier, the entire Phillips clan, loaded down with their various trunks, had taken a train to the city of Portsmouth. There they boarded a small steamer that took them to the island, which was located a few miles off the coast. Their final destination was the town of Freshwater on the Isle's remote western end.

The family spent a couple of glorious weeks basking in the sun. The hotel where they stayed, The Albion, was just steps from the beach, so Jack spent much of the time swimming, or combing the beach for sea glass and intact shells.

Jack loved the smell of the warm salty air, and he was fascinated by the expansiveness of the blue-gray Atlantic Ocean.

He also got a particular thrill each time he caught a glimpse of a giant steamer passing ghost-like offshore.

One day, his father rented a carriage and took the family on a sightseeing trip to the Needles, which were located on the western-most tip of the island. The Needles were a breathtaking series of rocks that jutted out into the ocean in nearly a straight line. Since the rocks had long been a navigational hazard, a lighthouse had been constructed atop the most distant one to warn off sailors.

Jack's father had discovered that the best place to view the formations—and the remote lighthouse—was from the grounds of a luxury hotel on the top of a nearby bluff.

After taking in the sight, Jack's mother and sisters went off to explore the hotel's gardens, while he and his father paid a visit to the telegraphy office that had been set up at the hotel.

The office wasn't fancy. It was just a small room with a desk and a man hunched over some equipment. However, Jack's father spent several minutes talking excitedly with the chap, whom Jack learned was a telegraphist.

From what Jack could gather, the hotel's telegraph office was not like the ones usually found in post offices. Its operator was exchanging messages with a similar station back on the mainland—without the use of telegraph wires. The signals, apparently, were being transmitted through the air, the fact of which impressed Jack's father greatly. He continued peppering the young operator with questions.

Jack learned that the wireless apparatus had been invented by an Italian man named Marconi, who was conducting tests in order to prove to the British Navy how useful this form of communication could be.

Jack found the wireless machinery fascinating, especially the apparatus the operator called the "spark-gap transmitter," which created a jagged, glowing bolt of electricity (resembling a miniature lightning strike) that zipped through the air each time the telegraphist pressed down on his lever. (This lever, Jack also learned, was called a "key.")

But the novelty of actually *seeing* electricity wore off quickly, and Jack grew bored. He was thinking—with longing—about the beach near the family's hotel. He hoped they'd get back in time to for him to take a swim before dark. Needless to say, he didn't dare express an inkling of this to his old man.

He nevertheless got his wish. The family returned to their lodgings by mid-afternoon, and Jack was able to take his swim. However, something of the visit to the hotel's telegraphy office stayed with him, because soon after the vacation ended, Jack announced to his parents that he wanted to become a telegraph operator himself.

And although it wasn't something he actively considered, perhaps his decision had something to do with the fact that he'd seen his father treat the hotel's young telegraphist with the utmost respect.

But whatever the reason, this one simple pronouncement became the turning point in Jack's life—and ironically, ended up sealing his fate.

CHAPTER SIX

STRANGE TEARS

Paul, Encino and West Hollywood, CA, 1996

As I continued to mull over the hypnotic regression, *Put to the Test* was soon "in the can"—which is producer-speak for "shot on videotape." The stories we eventually settled on were: 1. a psychic "doctor," who claimed he could remotely diagnose a patient's maladies—armed only with their name and date of birth; 2. a psychic detective, who said she received "impressions" of a crime by merely looking at police photos and evidence; and 3. a dowser, whose divining rods could supposedly locate buried sources of water.

In the end, the "doctor" and the "detective" were at least partially vindicated. After their readings were independently examined by experts, it was determined that, although they hadn't gotten everything right, some of their hits were so on target they could only be described as spooky.

However, the same couldn't be said for the dowser— failed in several attempts at finding the hidden water t producers had buried. But at least the guy had a sense of humor. When asked how it felt to have flubbed our test, he quipped: "Some days you get the bear, and some days the bear gets you."

I made a point of remembering that one.

By this time, my researchers and I had been given another assignment—a pilot for CBS called *The Searchers*. The show was about people who were looking for things: discoverers, explorers, treasure hunters, etc.

One of my researchers ended up tracking down a man who was trying to mount an expedition to find a long-lost cache of riches that has been missing since World War II. Since he sounded promising, I got him on the phone.

"So what makes you think you know where the Nazi gold is?" I asked.

The blustery gentleman on the other end of the line droned on and on as I jotted down notes, pausing occasionally to interject the obligatory "Uh-huh, uh-huh" or "And now, what makes you think that?"

In short—it was just another day at the office.

— — —

In some ways, it was probably a good thing I didn't have lots of time to obsess about the past-life regression. I'd always ~~~ ʲⁱᵒᵏⁱⁿᵍˡ'⟩ that introspection was the luxury of t least, *the underemployed*—and in the neither. I had all I could handle to navi-esses of the job.

another thing, too. In the weeks follow-had no further spontaneous flashbacks.

Even so, my mind would occasionally replay the strange, vertigo-inducing "sinking"—and the other images I'd seen while under hypnosis.

In the end, I came to the conclusion that the phenomenon might be real...that these could, in fact, be "memories" from my past lives. I think it was the combination of the two lives that convinced me. While the *"Titanic"* scenes, on their own, could be explained away as wish fulfillment, the same couldn't be said of the native's sad demise. And to my way of thinking, if one was an authentic past-life experience, both had to be.

I knew many people—particularly Buddhists and Hindus—took reincarnation as a matter of faith. I figured it wouldn't hurt to consider the possibility that they might be on the right track. As a lapsed Roman Catholic, I felt I had little to lose.

But there was more to it than that. I'd always been interested in religious thinking, and one of the things that bothered me about Christian belief systems was the concept that everyone would ultimately be judged on the basis of a single lifetime. I never thought this quite fair, since birth circumstances varied radically. How could a kid who entered this world in a crack house be held to the same standards as someone born into a family of loving, God-fearing philanthropists? So the idea of living a *series* of lives—which provided time to learn and work things out—appealed to me because of its innate sense of fairness.

As I grappled with this new, more spiritual way of looking at the world, work continued—as it always did—with me bouncing from show to show. By the summer of 1996, *The Searchers* had come and gone. The Nazi treasure hunter—not surprisingly—was unsuccessful. All he'd managed to unearth were a series of massive holes in Germany's Black Forest. And to top it off—actually there was trouble because *he didn't top it off*—he incurred the wrath of local forestry officials when he tried skipping town without filling in the holes.

Once this potentially embarrassing international incident was sorted out (he filled them in), legendary actor George C. Scott was hired to do the show's Voice Over. As was customary, I was present at the recording session—armed with my research notebooks—in case Mr. Scott challenged any of the facts in the script. This was standard operating procedure, the lesson of which I'd learned years earlier when I was a researcher on the daily magazine show *Hard Copy*.

It was a painful lesson. One day during a Voice Over session, Terry Murphy, the *Hard Copy* host, had balked at a factoid I'd written, insisting the figure attributed to the annual sugar consumption by an average American was too high.

"That can't be right," she exclaimed. "I don't eat 152 pounds of sugar a year. I don't know anybody who eats 152 pounds of sugar a year! Where did we get this figure?"

My initial reaction—which I wisely kept to myself—was, "Yeah, people from Beverly Hills don't eat that much sugar, but we're talking about the rest of America here...."

However, since I didn't have the research file to back it up, I found myself running to my office to grab it, while Terry and the crew stood waiting.

Although I was annoyed, I couldn't really blame her. Like most talent, Terry was conscientious. She wanted assurances the facts she was reading were actually correct. As one of the producers later told me, "It's her face up there on screen—and she's gonna take the heat if she says something wrong." It was a rookie error on my part, and I kicked myself for not having brought the file in the first place. I wouldn't make that mistake again.

In the end, though, it didn't matter with George C. Scott, who never challenged any of the statements in *The Searchers* script. He delivered each line as if he'd rehearsed it—and the reality was, he probably had. He was such a pro, and it was a great thrill to be in the presence of the *Patton* star—even if, truth be told, he didn't look too good. He'd lost a significant amount of weight since the last time I'd seen him on-screen.

At one point during the session, Scott's agent, who was sitting next to me, leaned over and said the actor had just been cast to star as *Titanic* captain E.J. Smith in a new NBC-TV movie about the disaster.

As I watched the frail and painfully thin Scott reading his lines inside the recording booth, I remember thinking he didn't look a thing like Captain Smith.

. . .

Naturally, after deciding my past-life "memories" could be real, I was unable to leave it there. I began to wonder if it would be possible to validate the experience by tracking down information about the persons I might have been.

I knew that finding the remote island where the native had been speared would be a next-to-impossible task—given the lack of specific detail I'd seen regarding him.

But *Titanic* was different. A lot of documentation about her passengers and crew existed. More than 1,500 people went down with the ship, and—assuming my terrifying rollercoaster plunge had been a real memory—I'd been one of them.

But who?

Looking back, I realize I should have just gone ahead and booked another session with Janeen—even if I had to pay for this one myself. However, the reason I didn't is not because I was being cheap. I think I was still freaked out by what I'd seen. The sinking flashback still played vividly in my mind, whenever I wished to recall it, which wasn't often.

The less scary path to take was the one of least resistance. With all the *Titanic* books lying around my apartment, what could it hurt to take a look through them again? Perhaps I'd connect with a particular victim's story...or have my memory jogged by staring into the eyes of a person in an old photograph.

However, as luck would have it, I was soon pointed in a particular direction—and I didn't even have to crack a book to do it. Not long after my hypnotic induction, a rarely seen 1958 British film was finally released to video: *A Night to Remember*, the first cinematic adaptation of Walter Lord's book. Unlike the various Hollywood retellings of the story, this version was told in a straightforward documentary style, illustrating the actual lives of many of the ship's passengers and crew.

The timing couldn't have been better. Just as I was in the market for a refresher course on *Titanic*'s victims, the *Night to Remember* video appeared in stores.

When I sat down to watch the film with my partner Pat McFadden, I realized that, as much else as I knew about *Titanic*, my only other experience with *A Night to Remember* had been when the book was read to my 2nd grade class, and I consciously remembered very little of it. I cracked open a beer and raised it in the general direction of the TV, while Pat started the tape.

About halfway through the movie, something unusual happened. When *Titanic*'s radio operator makes contact with the wireless operator of the *RMS Carpathia* (the ship that would heroically steam through the night to rescue survivors), I began to cry—and hard. The scene had no dialogue—all you hear is the dit-dot-ditting of *Titanic*'s wireless—and yet, tears were literally pouring from my eyes.

Thankfully, Pat was too engrossed in the movie to notice my bizarre reaction, which reached a crescendo when *Carpathia*'s wireless operator barged into the cabin of the ship's commander, Captain Arthur Rostron, to awaken him with news of *Titanic*'s predicament.

My crying jag, however, ended as abruptly as the scene, and as I wiped the tears from my eyes, I wondered why this particular sequence had packed such an emotional wallop.

I should point out I'm not generally the movie-weepy type. Oh sure, in my indiscriminant youth—actually, my teen years—I did cry when *E.T.* died, but this was a rare occurrence. Since I studied filmmaking in college, I tended to watch movies clinically, oftentimes rolling my eyes when directors blatantly attempted to pull the heartstrings.

So sitting there sniveling in my darkened apartment, I knew what I was experiencing wasn't normal.

An hour later, the film ended, and Pat shuffled off to bed. I sat alone for several minutes thinking about it. The film's climax had been a letdown. Given my earlier crying jag, I expected to have an emotional response to the sinking scenes. But my eyes remained dry when the great ship finally disappeared. And yet, for some reason, the much more innocuous wireless scenes had caused a meltdown.

A couple of days later, I sat down to watch the film again—this time alone. My reaction was the same—if not worse. Right on cue, I began crying at the same scene. (I've seen the film five times now, and, even today, I can't get through it without weeping at that part.)

The next day, I finally came clean with Pat about my reaction to the movie. He suggested we watch it again so he could see my response.

We popped in the tape and, an hour later, my tear ducts were on overload.

Pat studied my water-streaked face for a moment.

"That's weird," he said. (Pat is the master of the understatement—which I envy.)

As I removed the tape from the VCR, I began to wonder: is it possible I'd been one of the ship's wireless operators? On the surface, the idea kind of made sense. In the early 1900s, a young man interested in Mass Communications might naturally gravitate toward becoming a wireless operator aboard one of the great transatlantic steamships. This was cutting-edge technology at the dawn of the electronic age. However, if the same boy were born in the latter part of the 20th Century, it's perfectly reasonable to assume he'd aspire to become a film director or television producer.

Later, I did some Internet research on *Titanic*'s wireless operators. I learned that Junior Marconi Officer Harold Bride was 22 at the time of the sinking but survived. He died in Scotland in 1956.

Since I was born in 1963, I couldn't rule him out. But it seemed unlikely because he hadn't gone down with the ship.

Senior Marconi Officer Jack Phillips, however, had died in the sinking.

After downloading a black-and-white photo of him from the web, I spent several minutes staring at his face. He was handsome, but I had to admit I felt no real connection.

On the other hand, I was pretty certain he had blue eyes; in fact, I could see them clearly through the black-and-white photo.

And then I learned something else about Phillips: he was 25 years old when he died. He'd actually celebrated his final birthday aboard *Titanic*, just three days before the fateful encounter with the iceberg.

This freaked me out, because I'd always had this strange premonition I'd die young. And it wasn't some generalized fear, either. On the contrary, it was very specific: I was convinced I wouldn't live past my 25th birthday. This was the reason I'd actually waited until I was 25 and a half to move to California. When the quarter century mark—which had loomed so ominously in my mind—passed without incident, I figured there was no better time to pursue my dreams.

I didn't tell anyone about the premonition—certainly not before (I could see no good reason to), or after (given that I was proved wrong)—but I never found a satisfactory explanation, either, as to why I'd believed it for so long.

However, glancing once again at the black-and-white photo of the (I have no idea how I know this) blue-eyed, Jack Phillips, I wondered if the answer to that question was, quite literally, staring me in the face.

Titanic's Senior Marconi Officer,
John George "Jack" Phillips

Photo courtesy of the National Archives, UK

CHAPTER SEVEN

THE STORM

Jack, North Atlantic, September 1906

Jack was at sea, during a raging hurricane, and he'd never been so scared in his whole life.

He was alone in the Marconi Room of the *RMS Teutonic*, which was more or less a shack situated on the Boat Deck behind the ship's first funnel. Since the *Teutonic* had been built before the existence of wireless technology, the shack where Jack found himself had been added later. As he listened to the roar of the wind outside, he hoped the carpenters had known what they were doing.

Behind the shack, electrical cables stretched up to connect with two antenna wires that ran high above the deck. These aerial antennas, strung between the steamer's first and second masts, allowed for the transmission and receiving of messages.

Jack shuddered to think what would happen if the wind caused the antenna lines to snap. Being on the ocean, in the middle of a storm, without any means of communication, was not a desirable position for a ship to be in.

As the sheeting rain once again began pounding, Jack felt it couldn't have been louder—even if they were back at the shipyard and a hundred riggers were simultaneously hammering the shack's metal roof.

Jack attempted to adjust the volume of his headphones, as the vessel gave another sudden, nasty lurch. This was followed by the sound of retching from the adjoining room. When it was over, a male voice shouted, to no one in particular, "Jesus H. Fucking Christ!"

Jack was hardly shocked at the language. He'd heard all sorts of colorful expressions since arriving in Liverpool earlier that year—and he'd used similar ones himself on more than one occasion.

But as the ship began vibrating once again, causing Jack to grip the table in front of him for support, he wished he could smoke. A cigarette, he knew, would calm his nerves. However, smoking outside would be quite impossible now, and his boss, who didn't indulge (and was currently puking his guts out) wouldn't appreciate him lighting up in the Marconi Room.

Jack wondered what his dear old mum would think, if she could see him, smoking and cussing like a sailor. He was sure of one thing though: she'd die of fright if she were with him at this particular moment.

Glancing at the wall clock, he realized it was dinnertime back home. He could picture his parents, having just closed up shop, sitting down to supper with Ethel.

He wondered what they were talking about…the news of the day…or perhaps the contents of his most recent letter.

And, as he tried not to think about the ferocious storm—he wondered if they missed him.

— — —

Jack had left home six months earlier. The day of his departure was uncharacteristically sunny—given it was February—and his parents had walked him to the train station.

Jack was elated, and just a little bit nervous. He'd traveled alone by rail many times before—mostly to visit his sister Elsie or his aunts in Trowbridge—but this journey would be a lot farther.

Once the train arrived at London's Waterloo Station, Jack would have to switch tracks and take another to Liverpool, a city hundreds of miles to the north. Liverpool was the hub of Britain's oceangoing trade, and it was from its massive seaport the great steamships departed for America and the rest of the world.

As the train began rolling from the station, Jack watched his parents from the window. His mother waved frantically, while his old man stood stiffly. Jack noted, however, what appeared to be a faint smile on his father's lips. But he wasn't sure whether the old man was expressing relief to be finally rid of him, or whether his smile represented a modicum of parental pride in—or *at least grudging respect for*—Jack's accomplishments.

He hoped the latter was the case.

The rancor that had been created in the wake of his quitting school had subsided by the time he was hired by the post office, and was more or less buried when he began training as a telegraph operator.

As it turned out, Jack didn't have to spend too many months delivering telegrams before becoming a full-time telegraphist. The regular operator, a cherubic-faced, heavy-set woman, had been promoted to assistant postmistress, and Jack was summarily groomed to take her place.

For Jack, the hardest part of the job was having to learn Morse Code, which was not unlike a new language. Each letter and number was represented by a specific sequence of dots and dashes.

It took a while, but he eventually got the hang of it. Sending was easy. One simply pressed down the telegraph key—using the thumb and forefinger as leverage—and, as soon as contact was made between it and the metal plate below, a tone sound was created. How long one held down the key dictated whether one transmitted a dot (shorter time) or a dash (longer time). Since Jack usually had a written message in front of him while he was transmitting, he found it easy to translate the text into code as he went.

Discerning incoming messages, on the other hand, was more difficult due to the lack of visual reference. It took a great deal of concentration to recognize the flow of dots and dashes coming over the headphones and translate them correctly—especially if they were being transmitted quickly, which was often the case. A good telegraph operator could send 25 words a minute or more—an impressive feat when you considered it might take three or four keystrokes to transmit a single letter.

Jack was grateful the assistant postmistress had been patient with him as he learned the ropes. She'd taken the time to answer questions and gently correct his mistakes. And as Jack's speed and accuracy increased, his mentor seemed as pleased with his progress as he was.

Jack spent almost three years at the post office. He liked the job enough, certainly the independence of it—but he quickly grew restless. For him, the telegraph represented a tantalizing keyhole to the rest of the world. He received messages from all over the country—and occasionally foreign lands—and Jack found himself imagining what the places on the other end of the line were like.

During the course of his work, he began hearing more and more about the continued success of Guglielmo Marconi, whose invention was now being installed on nearly every ocean-going vessel. When Jack learned Marconi had opened a school in Liverpool and was seeking experienced telegraph operators to be trained for shipboard work, he grew terribly excited. He wrote away for information at once.

Upon receiving the application, however, he was disappointed. Enrolling at the school was expensive, and to make matters worse, students were required to purchase their own uniforms in advance.

Given he couldn't expect—nor would he have asked—his parents to lend him the money, he didn't apply right away. However, he did begin to save. And whenever he was tempted to spend needlessly, he remembered the application buried in his desk drawer.

He didn't tell his parents about his plans, although he did eventually share them with his co-workers, especially after they caught him reading—and rereading—the Marconi school correspondence. But for Jack, it was fun having a secret goal to focus on.

After two years of dedicated saving, he finally had enough money. He sent in his application—using the post office as a return address—and anxiously awaited a response.

One day, one of Jack's co-workers, a funny old chap with a big belly and large red nose, came to the half-door.

"Jackie boy," he said, "I've got a letter for you from the Marconi Company...."

Glancing up from his work, Jack stole a quick glance at the assistant postmistress, whose desk was next to his. She smiled excitedly at him.

The co-worker handed Jack the letter, and soon there was a group of people gathered around his desk. Jack turned the white envelope over in his hands. It seemed so official.

"Well, open it already!" the co-worker said.

Taking a deep breath, Jack extricated the letter.

"Dear Mr. Phillips, Your recent application to the Marconi School of Wireless Telegraphy has been accepted...."

Jack let out a sigh of relief.

"Well?" the co-worker asked.

Jack shared the news—and there was a large burst of applause. The assistant postmistress gave him a hug.

"I'm so proud of you!" she said.

As Jack received congratulations from his co-workers, the man who'd brought the letter disappeared to spread the good news to the rest of the office. He reappeared moments later with a bottle of alcohol.

"'Tis cause for celebration," the man said—although, given his large rummy's nose, it was generally known the man indulged in such celebratory moments often. The postal workers passed the bottle around and toasted Jack—again and again. By the time he left work, he was more than a bit light-headed.

Jack raced nearly the entire way home—a distance of two miles. He had no idea what his parents' reaction would be. He hoped there wouldn't be any problems—but, frankly, he didn't care if there were. His mind was made up.

As it turned out, both parents were delighted for him. His mother was happy because she knew it was something he really wanted, and his father, who was already impressed with Marconi's work, was even more impressed that Jack had been able to raise the money for school himself.

When she learned about it a few days later, Elsie too was thrilled. The only person in the family who seemed depressed about the news was Ethel, who'd not been feeling well on the day of Jack's departure, so she hadn't accompanied their parents to the train station to see him off. However, Jack didn't dwell on it; long ago he'd stopped trying to figure her out.

. . .

He did well in Marconi school, graduating six months later, near the top of his class. Right away, he was assigned to the *Teutonic* as second Marconi officer. But the job wasn't idyllic, since Jack didn't like his boss (the ship's first officer) very much. The man, who was just a few years older than Jack, lacked a sense of humor. He was also a stickler for rules and regulations, and he often irritated Jack by reminding him to do obvious things.

To his credit, however, the first officer did allow Jack to step onto the deck as the steamer got underway. Since it was his first voyage, Jack excitedly joined the throng of the passengers lining the railing, as they giddily waved to family and friends on the dock below. Despite the fact that Jack didn't have anyone seeing him off, he nevertheless found himself waving unabashedly along with the crowd.

During the crossing, his job mainly consisted of clerical work and delivering messages, although he did get to monitor the Marconigraph by himself during the early morning hours when the first officer was resting.

Overall, he was happy with his performance. However, he did get into trouble with the first officer once. It happened shortly after leaving Liverpool. While typing up a passenger message, Jack, to relieve his boredom, made a smart comment about its content. The first officer wasn't amused, and he took off his headphones and began lecturing Jack about the fact that Marconi messages were private, and reading them was akin to reading someone's mail. Although Jack was put off by the man's "holier-than-thou" attitude, he nevertheless accepted the criticism and took the message to heart, so much so that the day would eventually come when he'd say something similar to his own second officer.

The voyage across the ocean was relatively uneventful, but things were completely different on the return crossing.

Jack first became aware of the danger when a series of weather reports began coming in over the Marconigraph, saying that a hurricane, which had been wreaking havoc hundreds of miles to the south in the Caribbean, had unexpectedly veered north and eastward, and was now on a collision course with the North Atlantic shipping lanes.

Since it was Jack's job to deliver the Marconigrams, he'd had to repeatedly scurry to the bridge, and hand each message to the skipper personally. During one such excursion, the old man had winked at Jack.

"Hope that shack of yours is secure, Sparks," he said, after reading the piece of paper Jack had given him. "Wouldn't want it to blow off when the storm hits."

The captain smiled, but Jack wasn't sure if he was joking, or—in the face of a genuine threat—indulging in a bit of gallows humor.

When the storm finally made its appearance, three days after they'd left New York, it was like nothing Jack had ever seen.

The waves were like walls of water, and the ship's bow plunged threateningly each time it crested one and dropped into the trough behind it. Then, moments later, the ship would crest another wave, and fall again with a sickening thud.

Within an hour, the first Marconi officer came down with a severe case of seasickness. He retreated to the bunkroom, forcing Jack to cover for him at the Marconigraph. However, Jack had to admit the job was pretty easy, since he didn't have much to do except monitor transmissions. (With many of the passengers also sick—or else the junior Purser too afraid to bring their messages to the shack—Jack was in receiving mode only.)

— — —

He was slouched over in his chair, daydreaming about home, when a new message came in over the Marconigraph. He translated it quickly and instinctively.

It was another weather report, as usual marked MSG, or Master's Service Gram. After Jack copied down the message, he got up from the set. Since it was a Captain-to-Captain message, he knew it had to be delivered promptly to the bridge. He shivered at the thought. Outside, the wind howled ferociously, but the rain, at least, appeared to have stopped.

Jack poked his head into the bunkroom, which reeked of bile and sweat.

"Another weather report came in," he started to say, but was cut short.

"Well, take it to the bridge at once!" the first officer snapped, before rolling over and clutching his pillow to his head.

Jack didn't tell the first officer—although he wanted to—that he knew this, and that he'd simply come to inform him. And get his gloves.

After bundling up in his heavy overcoat, he headed out. The shack's door was practically blown off its hinges the moment it was opened, and it required a great deal of effort for Jack to latch it behind him.

Although the rain had abated, the wooden deck was still slick, so Jack found himself clutching the railing for balance as he made his way forward.

Hearing a metallic creaking noise nearby, he turned and noticed one of the ship's lifeboats had broken loose from its mount and was rocking back and forth in its cradle. It sounded like a rusty child's swing set on a windy day.

As Jack got closer to the bow, the wind definitely picked up, since the ship's forward funnel had been acting as a break, protecting the rear deck and wireless shack from a direct onslaught.

The increased velocity, however, made it extremely difficult for Jack to breathe. He found himself lowering his head and turning away from the gale every couple of seconds, in order to get some air.

When he finally arrived at the bridge, one of the deck officers helped him inside.

After pausing for a moment to catch his breath, Jack unbuttoned his overcoat and pulled the message from his pocket.

"Another weather report, sir," Jack said, handing the captain the piece of paper. The skipper glanced at it and slipped it into the pocket of his own jacket.

"How's it going back there, Sparks?" he asked.

"We're doing okay," Jack said. "Well, I am, at the least. The first officer is… a bit under the weather."

"Sick as a dog, you mean."

"Yes, sir," Jack said.

The captain laughed heartily. "Tell them message received, thanks."

"Right, sir," Jack said, and turned to go.

Then the skipper, perhaps noticing his pallor, winked at him. "Don't worry, Sparks," he said. "We'll make it."

"Of course, sir!" Jack said.

Jack bundled back up for the return trip to the wireless shack. Since the wind was now behind him, the going this time was easier.

As he took off his coat and laid it over the back of his chair, the first officer's voice called weakly from the bunkroom.

"You didn't tell 'em I was sick, did you?"

Jack paused for a moment, and then said "no" almost instinctively.

"Good," the first officer's voice continued, "'cause I'm feeling better now…."

His voice trailed off as the sound of retching once again filled the bunkroom.

Jack, who didn't say anything, was marveling at how a person so thin and gangly as the first officer could have so much vomit in him.

Returning to the Marconigraph, Jack sent the captain's response, and after getting the confirmation it had been received, continued monitoring the wireless traffic.

By evening, the storm had finally begun to abate. Jack spent the night at his station, and at daybreak, was happy to see that the sky—although cloudy—was definitely brighter.

The first officer soon emerged from the bunkroom. Pale and disheveled, he sat right down at the Marconigraph as if nothing had happened.

Jack took the opportunity to go outside for a long-overdue smoke. As he lit his cigarette, he saw the captain smoking his pipe further up deck near the bridge. When the skipper noticed him, he nodded—and winked. Jack smiled and nodded back.

After Jack had smoked his cigarette (two, actually) he returned to the Marconi Room. But the illness had put the first officer in an extremely foul mood. While Jack sat at his desk, the man made a point of thumbing through the logbook to see if Jack had made any mistakes during his watch. Jack was pleased to see that no mistakes were to be found. However, it was a Pyrrhic victory, since the first officer's attitude remained sour toward him for the remainder of the voyage.

But, as the steamer made its way back to England, the weather continued to brighten, which lifted Jack's spirits. From conversations he had with other crewmembers, he learned the storm they'd weathered—with only a few broken windows to show for it—had been larger and scarier than any other in recent memory.

Jack was proud of himself. He felt like he'd passed a really big test.

CHAPTER EIGHT

ARTIFACTS

Paul, West Hollywood & Long Beach, CA, 1996-1998

So now I had a name. Jack Phillips. Over the next year, I did computer searches every few months to see what I could learn about *Titanic*'s senior wireless operator. But I found precious little.

In early 1997, Phillips' name came up in an article from a German newspaper claiming *Titanic*'s salvagers—RMS Titanic, Inc.—had recovered the ship's wireless from the bottom on the Atlantic and put it on display at a museum in Hamburg, Germany. (Since then, however, I've come to learn that the article was erroneous. Apparently the writer had confused the ship's telegraph—used by the ship's officers to communicate with the engine room—with its wireless. However, I had no reason to disbelieve it at the time.)

My initial response upon reading this was maybe I should go to Germany to see it. A strong reaction might confirm my suspicions regarding a past-life connection to Phillips—or, conversely, a lack of one could show me that my feelings were just the result of an overactive imagination.

I knew I was dreaming, of course; a trip to Europe for such a purpose would be prohibitively expensive. Contrary to popular belief, mid-level Hollywood research directors don't make tons of money. However, I figured the exhibit would make its way to the U.S., and I'd eventually get the chance to see it. I couldn't help wondering, though, what sort of reaction I'd have, if I were in the actual proximity of the device.

Later that summer, I had the opportunity to view some other recovered items, when RMS *Titanic*, Inc. opened an exhibit at the *Queen Mary* in nearby Long Beach, CA. Although by this time I knew the wireless wouldn't be among them, I was nevertheless eager to go. Tickets included a walking tour of the fabled steamer.

The *Queen Mary* was one of the great steamships of the post-*Titanic* period. Built during the 1930s, it was decommissioned in 1967 and brought to Southern California, where it was turned into a floating hotel and convention center.

In order to provide visitors with a glimpse of the ocean liner's giant propellers, the *Queen Mary*'s outfitters had cut a hole in the hull and built a special room *that actually took visitors outside the ship*. Thus, you could look down into an enclosed pool and see a section of the ship's black exterior hull—and its massive port propeller—underwater.

Although I visited during the day, the scene was dark and eerie...the propeller lit by a garish green light. I had an instantaneous physical reaction: I became light-headed, my skin began to crawl, and I felt a rock in the pit of my stomach.

It wasn't just the horror movie creepiness of the setting—the close proximity to the ship's hull—and the sight of the water lapping against those steel plates—was simply too much for me. I nearly swooned.

Staggering back into the ship, I leaned against a doorframe to recover my balance. The tour guide saw my reaction and asked if I was going to be sick. Truth be told, it was touch and go for a while. But thankfully, my stomach eventually settled down.

Compared to the "excitement" of the tour, however, the *Titanic* exhibit was a disappointment. Frankly, it was cheesy. Most of the artifacts weren't restored. They were presented—like fish—in salt-water tanks.

One item that had been restored (and polished to a shine) was *Titanic*'s brass bell, which salvagers had cut from the ship's forward mast two and a half miles below the surface of the Atlantic.

It was the same bell *Titanic* lookouts in the crow's nest had clanged in warning after spotting the iceberg.

That was cool, and—as they say—worth the price of admission.

An even better admission took place in December of that year, when James Cameron's long-awaited *Titanic* was released. I'd wrangled tickets to a preview screening, and from the moment the film flickered onto the screen, with the faux black-and-white newsreel footage of the launch, I was swept away.

I spent the next two-plus hours with my jaw on the floor. When it was over, as my partner Pat liked to tell friends, I was speechless. And that's saying a lot.

I didn't have the same reaction to the wireless scenes I'd had during *A Night to Remember*, but that's probably because the Marconi officers received minimal screen time, and I was otherwise too busy being blown away by the stunning recreation of the ship to really focus on them.

However, one of the benefits of the film's unprecedented success was it brought a flood of new books on the disaster. I snapped them all up for my growing collection. One of these purchases was a compilation of Father Frank Browne's photographs from the actual voyage, and although I didn't know it at the time, the book would become quite useful later.

Father Browne, an Irish priest, had boarded *Titanic* at Southampton, but had only taken her as far as Queenstown, Ireland. Thus, when he disembarked, he had in his possession some of the voyage's only surviving photos. His pictures, which were eventually printed and reprinted in newspapers around the world, included the famous shot of the little boy spinning a top on *Titanic*'s deck. (Director James Cameron had cleverly recreated the image for his movie—as an obvious nod to Titanophiles.)

While *Titanic* continued to rack up record receipts at the box-office, business picked up for me as well. In addition to the slate of specials we were working on (for both ABC and CBS), there was a rumor going around that my boss was on the brink of signing a new deal to produce a high-profile series based on the *Guinness Book of World Records*.

One day, he cornered me in the hallway.

"Do you have a current passport?" he asked.

I shook my head.

"Get one," he said. "If we sell the *Guinness* show to Fox, we're sending you to London to go through their vaults for stories."

I was excited. I'd grown up idolizing—no, revering—the *Guinness* book, and I felt it would be a dream come true to work on a TV version of it.

"Do you think they're gonna buy it?" I asked as he walked away.

"Just get the passport," he said without turning around.

I was still grinning when I got back to my office. The prospect of a trip to Great Britain was certainly thrilling. I'd never been.

And there was that *other matter* as well. As I well knew, *Titanic*'s senior Marconi officer had grown up in England. In fact, he'd been born in a town not far from London.

"With a little luck," I thought, "I might be going on a *Titanic* research expedition after all!"

A few weeks later, we got the news. *Guinness* was a go. I was heading for London.

CHAPTER NINE

MARY

Jack, Clifden, Ireland, December 1909

Jack was sitting in his own pew near the back of the chapel. Ahead of him, the wooden benches were filled with families dressed in their Sunday finest. It was Friday night—almost Saturday morning—on the night before Christmas.

Jack was depressed. It was the second year in a row he'd been away from his family at the holiday. At least on the previous Christmas, however, he'd been joined by several of his co-workers, and the novelty of the experience made it seem like an adventure. But this year he was alone, which didn't please him at all.

For much of the service, he was lost in his own reverie. He could picture his parents' fragrant fir tree in the corner of the living room bedecked with tinsel and candles; the crackers laid out beside the silverware on the dining room table; and the smell of roast goose wafting in from the kitchen.

Suddenly, Jack became aware of a loud rustling sound. He realized the parishioners were getting up for the final hymn of the service. He had to practically will his feet to stand. He was reminded, once again, that he was stuck in a small Irish village hundreds of miles from anywhere, while his family gathered at home to celebrate without him.

The thought nearly brought him to tears.

. . .

Jack's first couple years as a Marconi officer had been a whirlwind.

Shortly after that scary transatlantic voyage aboard the *Teutonic*, he'd been transferred to another ship, the *RMS Campania*, which was owned by the Cunard Line. To Jack's delight, the testy first officer from *Teutonic* was not there; the man had been reassigned to a different vessel. (Jack hoped his gossiping to the ship's captain about the first officer's seasickness hadn't been the reason for the transfer—however, given the man's deplorable behavior toward him, Jack felt it would only serve him right if it was.)

Jack's new first officer was much more easy-going, which made their subsequent crossings far more enjoyable. Since Marconi men were generally left alone by the rest of the ship's crew—who viewed them with a certain amount of suspicion—it made all the difference to have a harmonious working relationship between the two. And Jack, who by this time was becoming more comfortable with the job, didn't miss the stress of having a fussy first officer watching his every move. Now he could relax and have fun.

But Jack quickly realized that the life of a Marconi operator was not unlike a vagabond's. He'd never be able to settle into the routine of any one officer pairing (no matter how pleasant) for long. Still—and despite the constant re-assignments—it was clear to Jack that his reputation within the Marconi Company was growing more and more solid. He ended up working as second (and, in one case, third) Marconi officer on a number of vessels—including the world's largest ships, *Lusitania* and *Mauretania*.

During this time, he returned home as often as he could, and when he did, he always received a king's welcome. His mother beamed with pride at the sight of her seafaring son—although this was hardly a surprise. Over the years, she'd always been a quiet source of support, and Jack was only too happy to repay her faith by living up to her expectations.

But since life with father had always been "different," he was genuinely shocked to learn—from Ethel—that the old man had taken to "immodest boasting" about him while he was away.

This change in attitude, while welcome, was a bit unnerving. For most of Jack's life, the sum total of his interactions with his former military officer father had consisted of brief lectures, or conversations that involved Jack saying "Yes, sir" or "No, sir." However, now that he was a world traveler, it seems the old man wanted to talk.

And not just talk...but *listen* as well.

Col. Phillips demanded detailed reports of Jack's travels, including descriptions of the ships he worked on, information about the ports he sailed into, and any pertinent gossip about crewmembers—especially officers and captains—whom Jack came in contact with.

Jack found himself staying up late with his father, long after the rest of the family had retired, answering questions over
a bottle of wine. (However, Jack always took care not to drink
too much, since he was well aware of alcohol's reputation for
"loosening lips," and he also knew that some stories would
never be fit for a parent's ears.)

But part of the reason Jack didn't fully let his guard down
was because he and his father were alike in many ways. Col.
Phillips viewed the world in terms of war, and often used
military analogies to describe ordinary, day-to-day skirmishes.
Jack, who'd come to view his environment in much the same
way, considered himself and the old man to be like opposing
generals. And now, although the "war" was over and the two
were enjoying genteel parlays at the treaty table, Jack felt it
would be imprudent to completely forget about their past conflicts, since history—as he'd learned from his father—tended
to repeat.

This was also the reason he was initially suspicious when
he noticed subtle changes in Ethel's behavior toward him as
well.

Since he was now contributing more to the family's fi-
nances—Jack sent home money whenever he was in port—the
cost of Ethel's medical care was no longer such a burden for
their parents. So perhaps it was to be expected that his big
sister's attitude would soften.

But Ethel's frequent letters were filled with more than just
gratitude. She spent a great deal of time faithfully recounting
the goings-on at home and in town. And while it was true that,
earlier in his life, Jack had resented these sorts of gossipy letters—especially the ones Ethel had written to Elsie

chronicling his indiscretions—now that he was on the receiving end, his thinking had changed.

He came to recognize them for what they were: a lifeline to the home he loved and the family he missed—much more so than he cared to admit. And when the ship docked at journey's end, Jack found himself looking forward to the small stack of envelopes—addressed in Ethel's impeccable penmanship—that were waiting for him.

However, the pivotal moment, when Jack first realized that a significant shift had occurred, took place one Christmas morning, after their mother had opened up the present Jack had given her. The gift, which had been Ethel's suggestion, was a framed portrait of him in his Marconi uniform.

As Mrs. Phillips squealed and clutched the photograph to her chest, Jack had glanced over at Ethel.

"Thank you," he mouthed wordlessly.

She nodded back, her lips curling in a warm smile.

An understanding of a sort passed between them, and in an instant, years of suspicion and rivalry began to dissolve, replaced instead by feelings of mutual respect, and even, Jack was happy to see, genuine fondness.

It was a very merry Christmas all around. Elsie had come home too, and there was much celebrating.

However, like clockwork, Ethel fell ill again right before Jack left, which put a damper on everyone's mood. To Jack, it felt like a light had been switched off. Ethel could barely raise her head from her pillow to say goodbye, and as he walked back to the train station, Jack thought crossly, "God only knows what makes her tick."

He wouldn't get an inkling for several more months, until he met Elsie one weekend in London during a layover. Elsie had taken the train to the city to meet him, and the two spent a couple days sightseeing.

One night over dinner, the subject of Jack's relationship with Ethel came up, and Elsie told him emphatically, "She loves you very much, you know."

"Oh, right!" Jack said dismissively, rolling his eyes as he drained his glass.

"It's true," Elsie said, as she paused to refill the wine. "You didn't know her...*before*."

Jack knew what Elsie meant. Before the meningitis that had hobbled Ethel, and taken the life of his older brother Fred.

Elsie went on to tell Jack that, from a very early age, Ethel had always wished to be a mother herself. In fact, from the minute Fred was born, Ethel had doted on him to excess (unlike Elsie herself, who'd always been more of a tomboy). And while the entire family had been devastated when Fred died, Ethel was hit the hardest, because she believed she'd caused his illness, having come down with the meningitis first. Jack felt a wave of gooseflesh at hearing this. It explained so much.

But then, Elsie continued, during the years between Fred's death and Jack's birth, Elsie had "prayed and prayed to God" to give her another brother. And when Jack finally arrived, no one was more delighted than Ethel, who lavished much love and attention on him during the first few years of his life.

"In fact," Elsie said, with a far-off look in her eyes, "she used to tell visitors that you were *her* baby. She hardly put you down."

"She did NOT!" Jack exclaimed.

"Yes, she did," Elsie insisted, recalling how Ethel would coo at him incessantly, and sing lullabies.

Jack was naturally surprised to hear this, as he had absolutely no memory of it.

However, Elsie continued, once Jack—*unlike Fred*—had progressed from an "adorable, helpless baby to a willful, bratty toddler, I don't think Ethel was prepared to deal with it."

Jack was shocked to hear this, on several fronts.

"I was NOT a brat!" he said at last.

"Of course you were," Elsie said, pausing to take another sip of wine, "and so was I. Why do you think we got on so well?"

Jack spent a great deal of time pondering his sister's words, long after he'd returned to the sea. But then, a few months later, in the spring of '08, his working conditions changed again.

He was offered a lucrative position at the Marconi Company's new land station that had been set up to transmit wireless messages across the Atlantic. Jack accepted the posting right away—despite the fact that'd he'd have to relocate to Ireland's remote west coast as part of the job.

His first journey to the Emerald Isle was eventful. After spending a night sailing from Liverpool to Belfast, it took Jack another two days to get across the country by train. It might have gone quicker, except for the fact that Northern and Southern Ireland had completely incompatible train systems. In fact, the tracks were built to different gauges, so travelers were forced to not only change trains, but in some places, stations as well.

"This is madness," Jack grumbled, after hauling his heavy duffle bag across Dublin. And naturally, Irish schedules didn't line up either, so Jack was forced to wait several hours for a train that would take him west.

The next day—after changing trains yet again—Jack noticed the topography of the land had also began to change: the endless rolling hills gave way to unexpected—and breathtaking—mountains.

The end of the line was Clifden, a tiny speck of a town located in a bowl-shaped valley surrounded by a dozen peaks. The bowl wasn't completely circular, however; to the west, the ring of mountains dropped away, revealing expansive views of the Atlantic Ocean.

As Jack later learned, the Marconi Company had been forced to build its transatlantic station in the far reaches of Ireland because the British Post Office, which held a monopoly on telegraphic messaging in the United Kingdom, had refused to allow the firm access to its landlines. This was a problem, since the sending of wireless transmissions across the ocean would only have value if it could then be connected to a land-based system. Thankfully for Marconi, the local Irish government—which held no such monopoly—was happy to let him build his station there.

Jack had been instructed, upon his arrival, to send a cable informing his supervisor. He did, and a short time later, a dilapidated wagon appeared to take him to the compound south of town.

The driver was an Irish boy in dirty clothes. His wagon was also filthy; it appeared to have been used recently to carry sod. Actually—Jack discovered as they got underway—the cart was generally used transporting peat that had been cut from the bog.

Jack learned that peat harvesting was the largest manned operation at the complex, since the station's furnaces consumed great quantities of it every day. Cutting peat was apparently back-breaking work, and the driver made it clear to Jack—several times—he much preferred ferrying passengers to his usual job. Jack couldn't imagine why.

Unfortunately, the Marconi compound was no more impressive at first glance than the bog cart that carried Jack there. The station house—where he would live for the better part of three years—looked decent enough, but the rest of the place had literally been built in a bog, with buildings occupying the random areas of dry ground. On the highest point of the property—a bluff overlooking the ocean—a large, fortress-like building had been constructed. It housed the Marconi Room, and the machinery required to run it.

Above and behind the building was the compound's most impressive feature: an aerial antenna that soared 200 feet into the air. Unlike ship's antennas, which were strung between the masts, this was a canopy of wiring supported by two parallel lines of wooden towers. The setup allowed messages to be successfully transmitted 2,200 miles away to a similar receiving station in Nova Scotia, Canada.

It didn't take long for Jack to acclimate himself to his new living situation. He would take meals and sleep at the station house, and then trudge back and forth to the Marconi Room for his shifts—which took place at all hours of the day or night. A lot of the work involved passing news stories back and forth across the Atlantic.

After a couple months on the job, the Station Master told Jack he was pleased with his performance. He was a silver-haired man with a kind face who was an unofficial father figure to the young operators. Jack grew to respect him a great deal.

In his living situation, he also had nothing to complain about. Meals were taken care of by the house cooks and his bedding was cleaned and his clothes washed by the staff laundresses.

Jack's only gripe had to do with Clifden's nightlife, which, by comparison, made Godalming's seem like New York's. Although the village had a few rustic pubs, Jack soon found he didn't care much for the clientele. He especially disliked the endless political discussions that seemed to erupt every time a Marconi man entered one.

While Jack was educated, he was not, as a modern person might say, politically aware. Thus, he was shocked to learn that several of Clifden's residents—especially the old timers who were regular fixtures at the pubs—were still upset about the Great Irish Potato Famine that had ended decades earlier.

Although Jack was naturally sympathetic to learn that the entire County Galway had been hit hard—the famine's many victims now filled Clifden's cemeteries—he was incensed to discover that many of the locals actually believed the British crown to be responsible for the famine.

After becoming involved in several heated arguments on the subject, Jack learned to stick with the other Marconi men and avoid conversing with the locals, no matter how pleasant they might at first appear.

For this reason, he generally kept to himself in the presence of the Irish, even going as far as to limit his interactions with the locals among the station's staff—since he suspected they harbored similar traitorous beliefs.

That's why it took almost a year for him to say more than a few words to Mary, a 17-year-old junior laundress with an infectious smile and cheerful personality, who always made a point of saying "Good morning" or "Good evening" to Jack whenever she encountered him about the station house.

In fact, Jack might have served his entire tenure at Clifden without speaking to her once, if he hadn't, in the middle of a shift, tipped over a bottle of ink onto his pants.

"Jesus Christ," he exclaimed testily, as he bent down to mop up the mess.

"Don't let the Station Master hear you say that," his co-worker said with a laugh, "or you'll be on the next train to Belfast."

"Right," Jack said, "Sorry...."

His fingers were now soaked with black ink, and even more troubling, his pants drenched with an assortment of spots.

After his shift, Jack went to the station house to change, and then carried his pants down to the laundry room at the back of the building. He was surprised to find the young laundress still on duty.

"Can I help you, sir?" she asked pleasantly.

"No, that's all right," he stammered. "I can do it. Just need to wash my trousers...spilled some ink."

"I can do it for you," she responded brightly.

Jack, however, was embarrassed, and insisted on washing the pants himself.

"Right," she said. "But you'll need hot water."

She was gone before he could say anything.

When she returned a few moments later with a steaming kettle, Jack thanked her and nearly splashed himself as he attempted to pour it into the tin bucket.

"Do you have some—" he started to say, but the girl was too quick for him. In an instant, she'd placed a bucket of soap in his hand.

As he scrubbed the pants in the soapy water, Jack became aware that the girl was continuing to glance over at him with a bemused expression on her face.

Finally, she broke the silence. "I didn't know you talked."

For a moment, Jack was unsure of how to respond. "Excuse me?" he said finally.

"Well, you don't really say much, do you?" she said, "I mean, I never actually hear you speak, except for an occasional mumble, so I thought...you could only...."

She began to mimic the motion of a telegraph operator working his key.

Jack's face flushed. He turned to her angrily.

However, as soon as his blue eyes met her lovely, green eyes ones, the girl burst into a fit of giggles. And Jack, although annoyed at the situation, found something infectious about Mary's laugh, and soon he, too, was roaring with laughter.

The Station Master popped his head into the room. "What's all the fuss?" he said, his eyes glancing about.

Jack explained he'd spilled ink on his pants and was trying to wash them.

"Well, let the girl do it," the Station Master said. "That's what we pay her for."

Jack got to his feet stiffly, while the smirking Mary took his place in front of the bucket.

After a few minutes of scrubbing, the girl lifted the pants from the soapy water. Her green eyes inspected them closely.

"I'm afraid they're ruined," she said gravely.

She turned out to be right, and eventually Jack had to buy a new pair in town.

However, from such an inauspicious start, a friendship was born. Thereafter, Jack made a point of saying hello to Mary, and, over time, even began seeking her out in the laundry room to exchange pleasantries.

The chief laundress, a thin, bird-like old woman, made it clear she didn't approve of such visits, although whether her concern was rooted in the interruption of work, or the unseemliness of Jack's presence, was never clear. She merely went about her business, her wrinkled face pulled into a grimace.

One day, Jack contrived to meet Mary outside while she was hanging laundry. After a few minutes of idle chatter about the weather (which had been rainy), Mary mentioned that a local waterfall would surely be running at full steam now. When Jack said he'd never heard of it, Mary insisted she take him there the next time her day off coincided with his.

"You'll love it," she said emphatically.

Although Mary usually had Sundays off, since Jack worked a rotating day-night schedule, it was a few weeks before their waterfall outing could be arranged. However, on a fine spring morning, they met in town after their respective church services, and set off on their hike.

Mary surprised Jack by bringing a picnic lunch, which she insisted on carrying for several miles, until it became apparent the basket was far too heavy for her. Jack eventually got her to relinquish it, and his arm was quite sore by the time they reached the waterfall, which was lovely, just as Mary had described. They spread out the food on a table-like rock.

Mary was not particularly beautiful; her freckled skin made her complexion ruddy, and her eyes and mouth seemed too small for her face. However, when she smiled—which happened more and more as the day progressed—her entire look transformed. Her best feature was the color of her eyes, which—as Jack had already noticed—were a unique shade of sea green.

Over the course of lunch, Jack confided in Mary about his various pub arguments, thereby admitting the reason for his reticence with her in the beginning—since he assumed she held similar opinions of the British crown.

Mary told him she didn't get involved in politics, so she didn't know—nor care—who was responsible for what. However, on the subject of mouthy pub rats, she definitely had an opinion.

"Those drunkards should be out making money for their babies," she said with disgust, "instead of sloshing it away in a pub. They're a bunch of good-for-nothin's."

Naturally, Jack was pleased to hear this.

After the hike to the waterfall, their friendly chitchat continued for several weeks. The next time their days off coincided, Mary suggested taking a rowboat out to one of the islands off the coast.

"You know how to row?" Mary asked.

"Of course," Jack lied.

Naturally, his fib was revealed shortly after they left the beach.

As Jack struggled with the oars, Mary grinned across the boat at him.

"Not much a sailor, are you?" she teased.

By this time, however, Jack was familiar with her sly humor, and while embarrassed, he wasn't actually offended.

With Mary's help, they finally made it to the island, which turned out to be farther than it appeared from land. On the rocky beach, Mary put down a blanket and laid out their lunch, while Jack relaxed for a moment to take in the view. The Marconi Station dominated the distant shoreline.

"Looks different from here, doesn't it?" Mary said as she served up the food.

As they ate, Mary asked Jack about his Marconi work.

"Well, there's not much to it really," he began, mimicking the keying motion Mary had teased him with earlier.

"Get off!" Mary said, with a grin.

Jack smiled, and suddenly had the urge to take her hand. But he resisted.

"Before I came here," he began, "I worked on steamers…"

"Which ones?"

"Some of the biggest ones really. Maybe you've heard of them: *Mauretania… Lusitania….*"

"I've seen pictures of the *Lusitania*," Mary said, clearly impressed. "It looks like a floating city!"

"Oh, it is," he said. "My quarters were on the top-most deck too, so I always had a birds-eye view of everything."

At Mary's urging, Jack filled her in on all the details he could recall about the ship.

"I suppose you've been all over the world, then?" she asked finally.

"Well, not everywhere," he said, "at least not yet. But I have been to Canada…and New York…."

"Ooh," Mary squealed, "tell me all about it!"

Jack obliged, and Mary listened with great interest. She told Jack that her brother—along with several aunts and uncles and their families—had emigrated to America, and while she herself yearned to go, her parents, who were getting on in years, refused to leave the family home.

"But couldn't you—" Jack started to say. She cut him off with a flash of her green eyes.

"They're not well," she said dismissively. "What would they do if they didn't have me to take care of 'em?"

Her voice trailed off. Jack could see watery specks appearing in the corners of her eyes.

In the brooding silence that followed, Jack had no idea what to say. After debating for several moments, he started to clear his throat, but then Mary turned to him, carelessly brushing aside her tears, and flashed an impish grin.

"To think you've sailed around the world," she said with a derisive laugh, "and I'm the better sailor!"

Jack's face simultaneously fell and flushed with embarrassment. In an instant, the day's merriment was over.

Soon they were heading back to the mainland. But the afternoon breeze had kicked up, and the water in the channel was rougher.

Given that Jack's pride was now wounded, he hoped to manage the rowing by himself. However, he was forced to accept Mary's help again when the choppy sea became too much for him.

Once they'd wrestled the rowboat onto the sand, Mary thanked Jack for a wonderful day. But Jack was in no mood to return the compliment.

"'Twas nice," he said half-heartedly, and left, trudging back to the station house without even saying goodbye.

As soon as he returned, the Station Master asked if he could have a word with him.

Bewildered—and slightly scared—Jack followed the old man into his study.

"I've been meaning to speak with you for some time," he said, as he carefully packed his pipe.

Jack's stomach flip-flopped. "What now?" he thought.

The old man's kindly expression suddenly turned serious. "What exactly are your intentions with that girl?" he asked.

Jack's face blanched; he found himself repeating the old man's words.

"What exactly are your intentions with that girl?"

"That's right," the Station Master said, lighting his pipe.

"You mean, Mary, I take it," Jack said.

"That's right," the Station Master said again.

"Well, I don't have intentions, sir," Jack stammered at last. "I mean, Mary and I are just friends. Or we were, I should say—"

His voice trailed off.

"Well, that's good to hear, my boy," he said, "because people are talking. They say it's quite unseemly for a young man to be carrying on with a girl without talking to her father first."

Jack was stunned on several fronts. In the first place, he was certain the old-biddy laundress was the one who'd been doing the talking.

And secondly: *carrying on?*

"We haven't…been carrying on, sir," Jack said adamantly. "She's just been showing me around, is all."

"I see," said the Station Master, although Jack wasn't sure he actually did.

The old man went on to lecture Jack about how he considered the "boys" to be like his own sons, and that he's merely acting on behalf of Jack's father. "What would he say if he were here right now?" the old man asked.

The question hung in the air.

Jack finally ended the interview by promising not to go on any further outings with Mary.

"Good boy," the Station Master said, and Jack was dismissed.

That night, Jack spent a great deal of time thinking about what the old man had said.

What exactly were his intentions with Mary?

Although he'd told the Station Master that he and Mary were merely friends, was that actually so? Had he, in fact, been courting her? Jack didn't think so. As he saw it, just when he'd grown to loathe Ireland, the two had met. They'd had a couple of pleasant afternoons together, and while it certainly made a nice change to have an outing to look forward to, this in no way meant he'd been *courting* Mary.

And even if he had been—which he hadn't—Jack told himself firmly, given the things Mary had said earlier, wasn't it clear she'd spend her entire life in Ireland, while he, on the other hand, had no intention of spending much more time here?

In the end, Jack reaffirmed the promise he'd made to the Station Master. And although he didn't admit it to himself, he was actually feeling a bit relieved by the decision. He knew there was another good reason why he and Mary wouldn't make an ideal couple—but he pushed *that unhappy thought* from his mind at once.

So, as he lay in bed, tossing and turning, Jack mourned the loss of Mary's friendship. However, he knew it was for the best. Their lives were simply too different for there to be any other outcome.

Thereafter, he suspended all impromptu visits to the laundry room, and made no further interceptions of Mary while she was outside hanging clothes. And although he remained cordial to her when she passed in the hall, he never lingered for long.

He knew Mary probably thought he was angry with her over her criticism of his seamanship; however, since there was no easy way of explaining the truth, he said nothing. The hardest part was carrying on while pretending not to see the hurt in her eyes—which he did.

After a couple weeks of these awkward interactions, it was Mary, not Jack, who decided to change tactics; now she was the one giving him the cold shoulder during their increasingly infrequent encounters.

But neither had an inkling that the time they were spending together—under the same roof—was about to come to an end.

In late summer, during an otherwise ordinary night, the receiving station across the ocean abruptly stopped responding. Later, the bad news came in over the landline; a fire in Nova Scotia had burnt the aerial's support towers to the ground.

There were several days of confusion, during which time no one knew what would happen. Then there was an unexpected guest: Guglielmo Marconi himself came to inspect the station and speak privately with the Station Master.

As the Station Master made the rounds to introduce Mr. Marconi to the staff, Jack summoned up the courage to tell his famous boss the story of his childhood visit to his station at the Royal Needles Hotel on the Isle of Wight.

Marconi seemed impressed by this, and told Jack that he eventually moved the station to a different part of the island, after the hotel's owners tried raising his rent. However, Marconi continued, the stingy innkeepers recently got their comeuppance…when an accidental fire destroyed their hotel.

Several of Jack's co-workers, who'd been hanging on Marconi's every word, began to laugh riotously at this, until they were silenced by a stern look from the Station Master.

"Of course," the old man said pointedly, "fire is no laughing matter, especially given our current circumstances…."

"Yes, that's true," Marconi said sheepishly, "but at least no one was hurt. Thank God for that."

Shortly after the inventor's departure, the Station Master assembled the staff for a meeting. He announced that several of them would be reassigned while the station across the Atlantic was rebuilt.

Unfortunately, many of the local workers would have to be sacked, including Mary. As Jack later learned, she'd burst into tears upon receiving the news.

"Great," Jack thought, "but why didn't they get rid of the old biddy instead?" He tried not to think about the fact that he himself might have played a part in the Station Master's decision to release Mary.

In the end, Jack was sent away for a few months, too. He spent the rest of the fall working as second Marconi officer on Allen Line steamships making runs from Liverpool to Boston and Montreal.

From time to time, Mary crossed his mind. He wondered how she was getting on…he heard she'd taken a job at the

Fever Hospital in town…and he also wondered whether he'd made the right decision.

In mid-December, he finally returned to Clifden. However, with the Station Manager away on an extended holiday with his family, Jack was left to fend for himself at Christmas.

– – –

Back at the service, the parishioners were singing "What Child Is This?"

Despite his depression, Jack found himself moved by the music. He tentatively joined in. He wasn't a bad singer; he'd been a chorist once, as a child, back at his family's church in Farncombe.

But the hymn ended all too soon—and with it, the service—and Jack felt his mood darken once again as he gathered his coat and lantern and joined the throng filing toward the door.

Outside the chapel, he stifled a yawn as he buttoned his coat. However, he knew his fatigue would be short-lived; the four-mile walk back to the station would certainly revive him.

Suddenly, the sound of another singing chorus drifted across the night air. Jack realized that the service at the nearby Catholic Church was still going on. He was annoyed. He couldn't help but notice that there were many more voices coming from that church, and as a proud member of the Church of England, he felt there were too many papists in Ireland.

But then he was struck by a different thought: *she's* probably in there.

He gulped.

Mary.

"So why not wait outside her church?" he thought.

It was an interesting idea. Surely, the service would be ending soon, and he could pretend he was just passing by. And if he saw Mary, and she acted like she didn't want to talk to him, he could merely wish her and her family a Happy Christmas, and be on his way.

"What would be the harm in that?"

Actually, he could think of several things, right off the top of his head.

He stood there, paralyzed by indecision.

The singing from the church began growing louder, and Jack knew the service would be over soon.

It was time to act: either wish Mary a Happy Christmas...or not.

After waffling for several moments, he chose not. He figured, after initial pleasantries were exchanged, there'd be an awkward silence, and he didn't wish to create bad feelings—for anyone—on Christmas.

Turning up the collar of his coat, he left. But during the long slog back to the station house, he started having second thoughts. He had to admit he missed Mary—and he cursed himself for not having the courage to speak to her.

Seeing a stone in the road, he kicked it, and watched as it clattered away down the street.

His melancholy had returned in full force, although he was aware that Mary wasn't the sole reason for it. During his recent shipboard work, he'd learned that several of his former classmates had been promoted to first Marconi officers on steamers. And although he knew he should be happy for them, a part of him felt jealous.

Jack was keenly aware that, in order to further his career, he'd have to return to the sea full time, which would also provide the side benefit of allowing him to visit his family more often.

He planned on leaving Ireland as quickly as possible. Although he'd already agreed to help the Station Master train the replacement staff for the reopening, once the place was up and running, Jack vowed not to be sticking around for long.

And he didn't care what the Station Master had to say about it!

. . .

Despite his intentions, however, Jack ended up staying in Ireland for almost another year and a half, the result of the Station Master's considerable powers of persuasion. The following Christmas, he magnanimously allowed Jack to take two full weeks to return home for the holidays.

Although Jack appreciated the time off, both he and the supervisor knew it wouldn't be enough to keep him in Ireland indefinitely.

In April of the next year, Jack, with the Station Master's blessing, was finally released from service. As soon as he got his walking papers, he was on the first train heading east.

A couple days later, he found himself steaming out of Belfast harbor. Across the river by the shipyard, a giant new liner dominated the view—White Star's latest floating palace, the *RMS Olympic*. Longer than *Mauretania*, and by all accounts more luxurious, Jack found the sight of this beautiful ship a positive omen, a literal manifestation of his hopes and dreams of returning to shipboard service.

There was another vessel nearby, but since it was still under construction and lacked funnels, Jack paid it little heed. All of his attention was now focused on getting home to England.

— — —

The steamer that had left Jack unimpressed was *Olympic*'s sister, built under the unassuming name of Hull #401. When she finally slid into the River Lagan at the end of the following month, the sight—as eyewitnesses would later say—was a spectacle to behold.

After a tremendous splash, the ship quickly righted itself, as a roar erupted from the throngs of cheering, stomping and clapping spectators who'd lined the streets for miles around the shipyard, on both sides of the river.

As the crowds began to disperse, an army of tugboats appeared and towed the newly born steamer downstream to the outfitting basin, where, over the next several months, she'd acquire her upper decks, her funnels, her distinctive coats of black and white paint, and her soon-to-be-famous name, printed in gold block lettering on her bow.

Her maiden voyage was eleven months away.

CHAPTER TEN

FIELD TRIP

Paul, London & Godalming, England, March 1998

I made sure my new passport was safe in my briefcase as I boarded the Virgin Atlantic flight. The deal had closed with the Fox Network to produce the *Guinness* show, and, as my boss had promised, I was being sent to London to do some research.

I was excited to be finally going to England!

My briefcase, which was now stowed in the overhead bin, not only contained my passport, but also a small manila research file I'd started a couple of years earlier. The folder was simply labeled "Jack."

Before I'd left, I'd gone back to the file to learn more about Phillips' hometown. Called Godalming, the town was located in an area known as Surrey, which was a short train journey south of London. [3]

The town's name is pronounced Guttle-ming, as I'd learned from a co-worker named Gareth Provan, a transplanted Brit. When Gareth heard about my supposed past-life connection to Phillips, he asked where Jack was from.

"I'm not sure how it's pronounced," I said, before proceeding to take a stab at it anyway. "Gaw-DAHL-ming?"

"It's Guttle-ming, dear," he said, rolling his eyes dismissively.

"Of course!" I thought, the second I heard the name rolling off his tongue. "Guttle-ming! That's it!"

However, his message was obvious. Had I really been Phillips, wouldn't I have known how to pronounce the name of the town where the guy grew up?

Gareth did have a point. On the other hand, who really knew how any of this worked? When I'd first seen the name in print, it had seemed foreign, alien. But Gareth's pronunciation had rung a bell.

And now, at long last, I was on my way to "Guttle-ming," to see what other bells—if any—the town would ring.

According to my research, Phillips was Godalming's most famous former resident. The young *Titanic* hero was still a source of great pride there. The town museum (called, appropriately enough, the Godalming Museum) even had an exhibit devoted to him.

---

[3] I later learned that Phillips was actually raised in Farncombe, a small village adjacent to Godalming, but which is generally considered part of the larger town.

Naturally, this would be my starting point. The printed web pages in my file contained the museum's address and hours of operation: Tues-Sat 10 a.m. to 6 p.m.

I couldn't wait to see the Jack Phillips exhibit. I also hoped to be able to purchase—at the Museum's ubiquitous gift shop—a Phillips biography. I'd been frustrated in my many attempts to find such a book online. But perhaps a local writer had written one that was only available at the Museum.

I knew I'd find out, one way or the other, when I visited Godalming the following weekend.

The plan was that my work at Guinness Publishing would finish by Friday—and since I didn't have to return to LA until Sunday, I'd have all day Saturday to explore.

In addition to visiting Godalming, I hoped to squeeze in a trip to Southampton to see Ocean Dock—where *Titanic*'s passengers had boarded at the start of their ill-fated journey. But, since Southampton was a long way off, I knew I'd have to remain flexible on that score.

. . .

My week in London passed quickly. However, an unexpected scheduling glitch forced me to adjust my weekend plans at the last minute. (I'd been invited to a business dinner on Saturday night, which I really couldn't refuse.)

When I got back to my hotel on Friday evening, I double-checked the map and discovered that Southampton was definitely out. It was simply too far away. But I would be able to visit Godalming and still make the work dinner—provided I took an early train the following morning. Even so, it would be tight. I wouldn't have much time for exploring. However, I figured the most important thing was to see the town—and spend a few minutes in the Museum's gift shop.

Naturally, I was at King's Cross Station at first light.

My train departed on schedule, and I took it to Guildford, the town that—according to my map—was the closest jumping-off point for Godalming. Leaving the station, I went down to the cabstand and hired a cab. By this time, I'd learned Brits called cabs "lorries." I told the "lorry driver" my destination, and off we went.

Thankfully, the guy was quiet, which was a relief, since I'm not sure what I would have told him if he started asking questions.

All was silent for several minutes as we drove. Then we made a turn, and as I stared out the window at the houses lining the road, an eerie sense of déjà vu settled upon me. My heart began to pound.

"Are we in..." I started to ask.

"Guttle-ming?" said the driver. "Yes, this is it."

I gaped in amazement as we continued down—what I later learned was—High Street, a long, sloping incline lined with cobblestones. The buildings and shops on either side of the road were small and crammed closely together.

"Wow!" I kept mumbling to myself. "This is it. This is it!"

A broad grin broke out over my face. The place was familiar. *I knew it.*

However, my delirium was short-lived. The cabbie pulled over suddenly.

"Here you are," he said.

I looked at the Godalming Museum, a small, unassuming building nestled between a shop and some sort of office.

"How long will you be?" the driver asked.

I knew I had—at most—a half-hour before I'd have to start back to the train station.

"About fifteen minutes or so," I told him.

"I can wait," he said.

"That would be great," I said. "Thanks."

I jumped out of the cab—my sneakers sure-footed on the cobbled sidewalk. However, as I approached the door, I noticed a small sign in the window: "Museum closed for renovations. Opening in April."

"Dammit!" I thought, after coming so far—and to be so close....

I saw the cabbie looking at me through the windshield. I didn't know what to do. I considered paying the guy and then setting off on foot to explore the town, but decided not to risk it, since I didn't know how difficult it would be to find another taxi to take me back to the train station on time.

Glancing once more at the strangely familiar street, I got back into the cab.

"Closed, eh?" the cabbie said. "That's a bit of bad luck."

I nodded glumly. I'd intentionally stayed away from the museum's website since learning I'd be coming to England. It had probably been a year since my last visit. Because the World Wide Web was still in its infancy at the time, the site had been primitive. The only photos it contained had been pictures from the "Jack" exhibit.

Since it had been my goal to see the town with my own eyes first, I hadn't wanted to be influenced by seeing photos of it in advance. In that, at least, I had succeeded.

However, now that I had, I wanted more. Would it be possible, I wondered, for me to locate the places where Jack had lived and gone to school—without any additional information?

"I'll never know," I thought remorsefully, as the cab sped up and the familiar street disappeared behind us. At least, not on this trip.

I found myself completely distracted as I boarded the train back to London. My mind, as well as my heart, was racing.

If only I'd had time to look around. I might even have found a Phillips biography in a local bookstore. But no such luck, thanks to that business dinner.

As the industrial-looking British countryside flew past my window, I turned the image of that familiar street over and over and over in my mind.

I didn't know it at the time—nor would I have been surprised if I had learned it then—but that particular road had remained virtually unchanged for more than a century. Elsewhere in the world, time had marched on. But on Godalming's High Street, it stood still.

I also wouldn't have been surprised to learn—as I later did—that *Titanic*'s Senior Marconi Officer Jack Phillips had spent more than three years walking up and down that very road, on his way to and from his job at the Godalming Post Office, which, in Jack's time, was located just a few doors down from the current location of the (Sorry, Closed for Renovations) Godalming Museum.

CHAPTER ELEVEN

BENNY

Jack, Liverpool and New York, September-November 1911

"Well, this isn't a good start," Jack grumbled, as he hoisted his duffel bag over his shoulder, and set out through the crowded streets of Liverpool.

His excitement over his latest assignment—as second Marconi officer aboard the *RMS Adriatic*, had dimmed a bit since his arrival, after discovering the entire city had ground to a halt due to a railroad workers strike. And worse yet, the Liverpool dockworkers had apparently also struck—in solidarity with the rail men—so *Adriatic*'s scheduled departure was delayed indefinitely.

Jack was incredulous. It seemed to him that while he'd been away in Ireland, the world had turned completely upside down. He assumed—in this case perhaps correctly—that the city's many immigrant Irish workers were behind the strike.

"What's this," he thought angrily, "inconveniencing the lot of us because someone's not happy with his wages? And what about my wages, which I won't be getting while I'm holed up in port? Why don't they just get another job and leave the rest of us alone!"

Jack ended up having to walk six miles to find overnight lodgings, toting his heavy duffel through the stifling and crowded streets of Liverpool, where tempers flared on every corner.

At one point, he accidentally bumped an elderly passerby, and the man began screaming insanely in his face. Invectives—mixed with spittle—flew everywhere. Jack's repeated apologies did little to calm the codger, and a brawl was only narrowly averted when a police officer arrived and sent the miserable pedestrian packing.

Thus, Jack was in a completely foul mood when he finally arrived at his destination: the army barracks north of town where Marconi officers often stayed during layovers. At first, the news there wasn't good either.

"All full up," the man at the gate said. "Sorry."

"Do you know if Benny Northcutt's here?" Jack asked.

The man's attitude changed at once. "Yes, Benny's here. Are you Jack? He told me to keep an eye out for you...."

"Good old Benny!" Jack thought, as the guard waved him through.

He found Benny, with his tousled brown hair, lopsided grin and his usual cigarette in mouth, in the middle of a card game in the bunkhouse.

"Jack!" he beamed, "You've finally made it! Make a place for him, boys...."

Jack was happy to see Benny. Right away, he noticed that his old friend had filled out, and lost some of the boyishness he'd had when the two had first met back at Marconi School. However, given Jack's exhaustion, he wasn't in the mood for socializing with a bunch of new people, so he begged off, telling Benny he'd rather get some sleep.

"I hope you don't mind sharing a bunk, then," Benny said.

Jack's face fell. Benny explained that every bed in the place was accounted for, since the barracks were being used to house out-of-town police officers brought in to help deal with the strikers.

Seeing Jack's expression, Benny said, "You can at least be grateful I found us this, though."

"I'll try," Jack thought, as he changed into his nightclothes.

Wedging himself against the wall to be as far from Benny as possible, Jack went right to bed, although sleep didn't come, and he was still awake later—although he pretended otherwise—when Benny finally crawled in beside him.

Soon Benny was snoring fitfully...which made it even more difficult for Jack to sleep. The air in the bunk was stuffy, and his senses were filled with the smell of Benny's exhales— which reeked of alcohol and tobacco. And as much as he tried not to notice it, Jack could also feel the warmth of Benny's back pressing against him.

Suddenly, Jack felt a different kind of warmth spreading to his groin area, and he was shocked to discover he was becoming aroused.

As he stared at the drab gray wall, with a painful tent in his pajama pants, Jack found himself silently repeating the word "no" over and over, but unfortunately, it didn't help.

– – –

Jack was pretty good at keeping certain parts of himself compartmentalized. But the truth was, he had—what today would be called—a "man crush" on Benny.

Jack had not been sexually active until he and Benny had met at Marconi School. And although they originally weren't roommates, when they became friends, Benny had arranged a switch so he and Jack could bunk together.

As Jack recalled, the payoff had involved alcohol and cigarettes, which Benny had proffered to their previously assigned roommates. Unlike Jack, Benny came from a well-to-do family, and he always had extra money for such things. At first, Jack, too, felt bad about being on the receiving end of Benny's largess. However, since Benny didn't seem to mind, he eventually stopped fretting about it as well.

Although Benny hadn't been the best learner in the class, he was handsome, outgoing and very funny, and Jack enjoyed spending time with him. Sometimes they'd celebrate the end of a long school day with a visit to a local pub, and stay up 'til all hours talking, laughing, and smoking. (It was Benny who'd first convinced Jack to take up cigarettes, which he enjoyed right away.)

However, the most significant thing Benny introduced Jack to was the art of self-pleasuring. The "lesson" had taken place a few weeks into their new living arrangement, after a night of serious drinking. Benny had jumped into Jack's bunk with a French lingerie catalogue he'd somehow acquired, and soon had his hand down his trousers, caressing his member.

Jack, still bleary-eyed from the booze, didn't find himself stimulated by the pen-and-ink drawings of the French women in the same way Benny clearly was. However, so as not to tip his friend off, he nevertheless dug his hand down into his own drawers and began some half-hearted rubbing. But Benny wasn't fooled.

"Aww, for Christ's sake," he'd whispered emphatically, "it's a dick, not a fish! You've got to grab a hold of it like this!"

In a flash, Benny's hand was down Jack's pants, and his penis instantly responded to the pressure Benny applied.

"There you go, see, you've got to put some elbow into it," Benny said, as Jack was suddenly overcome with a full body sensation of pleasure. "That's how it's done...."

Without warning, Jack climaxed in his pants, and Benny jerked his hand out with a laugh, before wiping up on Jack's shirt. And despite the fact that his clothes were now soiled, Jack suddenly found himself very sleepy. But Benny shook him awake.

"Now you've got to help me," he said. "It's always better when someone else does it...."

In the years since school ended, Jack had revisited this moment—and other subsequent ones like it—several times, but always at night, when he was alone in his bed, hoping for a little stress relief before sleep. After meeting Mary, Jack did try to change up the fantasy, imagining being intimate with her in the way husbands were supposed to be intimate with their wives—but it never quite worked, and long before the session was over, his mind, inevitably, returned to those long ago school nights with Benny.

And now, here Jack was, once again sharing a bunk with his old friend; although, based on some bawdy comments he'd overheard Benny making earlier (while he'd been feigning sleep), Jack was pretty certain things were different for Benny now.

Or were they?

He barely closed his eyes all night.

. . .

Despite getting minimal rest, Jack's attitude did improve the following morning—especially after wolfing down breakfast.

As he and Benny waited for word about when the *Adriatic* would depart, they wiled away the hours filling each other in on their lives since school. However, Jack's stories—even his recounting of the hurricane—didn't hold a candle to Benny's, which were much more interesting, and frankly, more outrageous.

Benny spoke of making several friendships with various crewmembers on board the ships he worked (which certainly hadn't been Jack's experience), and about the wild times—and parties—he'd taken part in while in port. Also, as Jack was unhappy to note, he bragged about the many women he'd been with.

"So you spent, what, three years in Clifden?" Benny asked, "How could you stand it? I would've gone bats."

"It wasn't so bad," Jack found himself lying. He didn't like the way Benny was acting as if his experiences had been the only interesting ones. With mixed success, he tried painting a picture of life in Ireland as endlessly entertaining.

"But there couldn't have been women..." Benny snorted.

"There was, actually," Jack started to say, but stopped when he saw the look of keen interest appearing on Benny's face.

"Awww," said Benny, "go on, spill it...."

However, Jack had no intention of telling Benny about his dealings with Mary, so he tried changing the subject.

"And of course, it was fun meeting Marconi..." he said casually.

After Jack relayed to Benny the details of his encounter with their boss, Benny seemed momentarily impressed. But then he launched into a lengthy discourse about having worked as second officer to none other than Jack Binns, who, as Jack well knew, was even more famous than Marconi was.

Binns was renowned for saving the lives of hundreds of passengers and crewmembers of the *RMS Republic*, which had sunk after being rammed by another vessel in heavy fog a couple years earlier.

Benny gave Jack a blow-by-blow of the harrowing events—purportedly relayed to him by Binns himself.

"He was sending the distress call the entire time the ship was sinking," Benny said, "and he didn't bail out 'til the water was clear up to his ears!"

"You don't say," Jack said, although at this point he was highly suspicious of Benny's tale. Of course, he had a great deal of respect for Binns—every Marconi officer did. The man was obviously a hero—he'd used the Marconigraph to summon rescue ships.

That said, however, Jack felt that Benny's story about Binns swimming away from the Marconi Room was clearly an exaggeration. The Marconigraph would have ceased to function well before immersion because the transformer, Jack knew, would have shorted out.

He chose not to argue though, since listening to Benny talk about Binns was definitely better than having to answer questions about Mary.

However, all too soon the Binns tale was spent, and Benny once again tried wresting the conversation back to the subject of Jack's exploits with Irish women.

But Jack refused to take the bait, and Benny finally gave up, albeit with a smug smile.

"Well, don't worry," he said with a wink. "When we get to New York, you'll forget all about what's-her-name...."

Jack ears suddenly burned with embarrassment. He had no intention of allowing Benny to pressure him into doing something he wasn't prepared to do.

But he told Benny none of this. And as his old friend suddenly began sharing details of yet another sexual adventure—this one, apparently, having taken place beneath New York's Brooklyn Bridge—Jack felt himself growing more and more disappointed.

It was clear that Benny had moved on—and he hadn't, and he had no idea what to do about it.

At the end of the day—and none too soon for Jack—word came to the station that a deal had made been made with the strikers, and the *Adriatic* would be cleared for departure the following day. Early the next morning, he and Benny hauled their bags to the Princes' Dock and boarded the ship.

The voyage passed uneventfully, although Jack found himself feeling a bit taken advantage of. As a rule, the second officer's job generally involved typing and clerical work, as well as spotting the first officer during the night, and filling in during the day for meals and occasional breaks. However, unlike other first officers with whom he'd worked, who were very professional and seemed unwilling to hand over the key except in an emergency, Benny was very casual about such things. He often disappeared for several minutes—or hours— at a time, returning with nary an explanation.

And while most first officers slept during the night, Benny was out and about for long stretches, oftentimes returning as late as sunrise with the smell of alcohol on his breath, which of course was a no-no.

As both he and Jack knew, shipping lines—including White Star—strictly forbade the consumption of alcohol by crewmembers while at sea. Since smuggling a bottle aboard was made impossible by the fact that their bags were inspected when they signed on at the outset of the voyage, Jack wondered who'd been supplying Benny with booze.

"Probably a lonely cook working the night shift," he thought. But he chose not to delve into the matter—as he had no wish to get his friend fired.

However, with Benny staggering into bed for only a couple of hours' rest on a nightly basis, Jack would generally have to wake him up for the start of his shift. Then the groggy Benny, leaning further on their friendship, would ask Jack to spot him for a few more minutes, which often turned into hours.

Jack didn't mind the additional work. He certainly preferred keeping busy, to the usual drill of waiting around for the first officer to give him something to do. But on the other hand, he resented that Benny was making almost twice as much money as he was, while he was doing the majority of the work.

Things didn't improve when they got to New York. As they signed into their temporary lodgings at a Mariner's house in Greenwich Village, Benny told Jack he planned to make good on his promise of finding him female companionship to help him get over, as he put it, his "lost Irish love."

"That won't be necessary," Jack said, but Benny, after giving him the once over, quickly replied, "Oh no, it's absolutely necessary."

That evening, Benny took longer than usual to prepare for a night on the town.

"Since you're ready and I'm not," he called from the washroom down the hallway, "go get me some fags. I'm nearly out."

Jack couldn't argue. Over the years, he'd certainly provided Jack with plenty of cigarettes.

When he returned from the tobacconist, Jack found Benny dressed and ready to go.

"But before we go to the pub," Benny said, "I need to visit someone. 'Twill only take a minute."

Soon the two were in the shadow of a run-down brownstone in the East Village.

"Just wait here," Benny said, before entering the dilapidated building.

Jack paced the sidewalk, smoked a cigarette, and wondered who Benny could possibly have known in this part of town.

A few minutes later, Benny poked his head from one of the brownstone's upper-floor windows and motioned for Jack to come inside.

Butting out his smoke, Jack entered the building's dingy and poorly lit lobby. To the left was a flight of stairs, and to the right a small clerk's window covered with wrought-iron bars. Jack walked over to it and saw a hard-faced woman sitting at the desk.

"Your friend's waiting for you upstairs," she said, handing him a tarnished brass key marked #11.

"What's this about?" Jack thought, as he began climbing the steps.

When he got to the second floor landing, he wrinkled his nose. The hallway in front of him smelled like cat piss.

Several yards down the corridor, he spied a door marked #11. He walked over to it and, summoning up his courage, knocked. There was no answer. He waited for a few moments, and then, not knowing what else to do, put the key into the lock. As soon as the door opened, the smell of heavy perfume wafted into the hall.

"Hello?" Jack asked tentatively. "Benny?"

"He's not here," said a female voice.

As Jack's eyes adjusted to the darkness inside the room, he could make out the figure of a woman, in a long dress, lying on a bed.

"I think there's been a mistake," Jack said, and began closing the door.

The woman spoke again. "Are you Jack?"

He stopped in his tracks.

"Benny told me his friend Jack needed some takin' care of."

"Wh--where is he?" Jack stammered.

"He's busy," the woman said with a hoarse laugh.

Comprehension slowly dawned on Jack's face, which soon flushed with fury.

"So, you gonna come in?" the woman asked.

"No," Jack said at last, closing the door softly. "I'm sorry."

Heart pounding, he stormed down the stairs and out onto the street.

"Hey, where's my key?" the woman in the window yelled after him, but Jack ignored her. He'd actually left it in the door, which he knew she'd figure out sooner or later.

As he lit another cigarette to calm his nerves, his mind remained focused on a single thought: *I'm going to kill Benny!*

— — —

During the return crossing, the tension between him and Benny remained palpable. Benny, who'd paid in advance for the prostitute, was livid that Jack had left so abruptly.

"Thanks for humiliating me," Benny said in disgust. "Damn waste of money you are!"

Jack knew he had every right to be furious with Benny for embarrassing him like that; however, Benny's comment also struck a nerve, since Jack had never forgotten the lopsided imbalance of their financial history.

He felt, by turns, rage and shame; but since he couldn't relay any of this to Benny, he remained silent.

However, as the voyage progressed, both of their attitudes began to soften. They started joking again, and Jack even considered apologizing to Benny, when things between them abruptly came to a head.

The night before the ship docked, while Jack was working his solo shift, he became aware of strange sounds emanating from the adjacent bedroom.

"Funny," Jack thought, "I don't remember hearing Benny return…."

But as the noises from the bunkroom grew louder, Jack realized that must have been intentional, because Benny was clearly entertaining a woman in there. And from the sound of things, neither had their clothes on. Jack was incredulous.

After putting up with the noises for what seemed like an eternity, Jack finally removed his headphones and went to the washroom. He even left the suite door open, figuring it would serve Benny right if a passing ship's officer caught him.

However, when he returned a few minutes later, no sounds emanated from the bunkroom. After pausing at the door for several moments, he flung it open, and there was Benny, alone, passed out in bed.

The nerve of that man, Jack thought, as he settled back at his desk. Right away he noticed his new fountain pen was missing. It was the kind that kept the ink inside without leaking. The pen had been a birthday gift from Elsie, and Jack knew she's spent a great deal of money on it.

Thus, he was perfectly livid, and as soon as Benny emerged from the bunkroom a few hours later, he confronted him about it.

"How do you know she took it?" Benny asked, rubbing his eyes.

"Who else could it've been?" Jack shot back.

"What's the big deal, anyway?" Benny said, stifling a yawn. "It's just a pen. I can buy you a replacement."

"No, you can't!" Jack shouted back. "Because it won't be the same one, and you know it!"

"A pen's a pen, Jack," Benny said dismissively, before sauntering off to the washroom.

A few hours later, when the ship docked and the two signed off with the Purser, Benny casually asked Jack if he planned on staying in Liverpool during the layover. Although it remained unsaid, it was clear to both this was the turning point for their friendship.

"I think I'll go home," Jack said at last, attempting to sound equally casual.

"All right then," Benny said a bit too brightly. "I'll see you in a few days."

For his part, Jack didn't mind that he'd probably be spending much of the break on trains to and from Farncombe.

"It wasn't just Benny," he thought. "It's Liverpool, too." Since the strike, he'd truly come to loathe the place.

Jack's visit home was very pleasant. Before he left the city, he'd sent Elsie a cable informing her of his travel plans. She ended up joining them at his parents' house. It was just like old times, and Jack enjoyed a couple nice days sleeping in and being pampered by his mother. The only downside was that Ethel had not been in the best of health. However, she tried to remain upbeat, so as to not bring the others down.

As usual, Jack stayed up late chatting with his father, who was just as outraged as his son upon hearing about the chaos in Liverpool caused by the striking workers.

At one point, after his old man had finished off a bottle of wine, he cleared his throat. "So," he said, "have you met any women during your escapades?" He smiled at Jack. "You know...." But then his voice trailed off and he winked slyly at his son.

Jack nearly spit up his drink.

As he coughed and tried to regain his composure, Jack quickly considered his options. Telling his father about his friendship with Mary was out of the question, although he did consider—briefly—regaling him with the story of his abortive visit to the East Village brothel. However, common sense prevailed. As pleasant as his father had become over the past few years, Jack wasn't sure he'd find this sort of story amusing.

"Not really," was all he ended up managing. "No one especially."

"I see," said his father.

"Well, it's getting a bit late, isn't it?" Jack said, draining the last of his wine and ending the conversation.

On the train ride back to London, Jack had an inspiration. Suppose he could arrange a permanent transfer to a ship—or ships—departing from Southampton? In the years since Jack had joined the Marconi Company, the port of Southampton had steadily grown more popular with transoceanic travelers, since the southern city was closer to London than Liverpool. (The side benefit of this for Jack was it was closer to Farncombe as well.)

If he could arrange such a transfer, Jack reasoned, he'd be able to live at home between voyages, eliminating the expense of out-of-town lodgings and long train trips. And the savings could be given to his parents to help pay for Ethel's care.

The more Jack thought of it, the better the idea sounded. He had to assume he had enough seniority within the company to at least request the transfer. Whether it was granted was another matter, but Jack could see nothing wrong with asking.

When he arrived in London, he went directly to the Marconi Company offices to speak with his supervisors. Although their response was noncommittal, Jack was nevertheless pleased he'd had the courage to submit his request. Thus, he was in good spirits as he boarded the train for Liverpool.

During his second *Adriatic* voyage, things between Jack and Benny settled down a bit. Both took great pains to behave professionally toward one another. For his part, Benny became more responsible and didn't slough as much of his own work onto Jack. And when they got to New York, he didn't pressure Jack into joining him for his nightly forays. Both assumed they'd be going their separate ways.

The same was true upon their return to Liverpool. Neither asked the other what their plans were, although both knew Benny would remain in town while Jack returned to Farncombe.

At least, that *had been* the plan, until Jack stopped at the post office to pick up his mail and discovered a letter waiting for him that wasn't from Ethel. The minute he saw the spidery handwriting on the envelope, his heart began to pound.

It was from his father. This was highly unusual. His father had never written to him before.

With trembling fingers, Jack opened the envelope.

"Dearest Jack," the letter began, "Your mother and I think that it's high time you were married...."

And it went downhill from there.

CHAPTER TWELVE

ICEBERGS

Paul, London and Greenland, March 1988

The morning after my trip to Godalming, as I took the taxi back to Heathrow, my mind was still wandering along that strangely familiar, cobblestoned street in Jack's hometown.

I'd read about déjà vu, of course, and heard the usual stories—how a person goes to a new place, or has a conversation with someone they've just met, and they're struck by the overpowering feeling they've seen the place—or had the same conversation—before. I knew scientific studies had even been conducted to explain the phenomenon, the conclusion of which was the brain registers things twice. However, I wondered if that was true in my case, since I'd never felt anything remotely similar until that weekend.

Perhaps I really *had been* Phillips?

A couple of hours later, as my jet headed out over the Atlantic, I couldn't help but think about how much the world had changed since 1912. The same journey from London to

Los Angeles would've taken weeks back then. First you'd have to take a train to Southampton—then board a steamer and spend six days crossing the Atlantic. And once you arrived in New York, you'd have to travel to Penn Station and spend another week crossing the U.S. by train. And here I was, about to make the same trip in less than eight hours.

Another seismic change between 1912 and 1998, of course, was the shift in societal attitudes toward homosexuality. Just a year earlier, popular comedienne and TV star Ellen Degeneres had proclaimed "Yep, I'm Gay," from the cover of *Time Magazine*. And although the battle for recognition and acceptance by gays and lesbians had been raging for years—mostly playing out in courtrooms, daytime TV, and the Op-ed sections of newspapers—Ellen's announcement catapulted the discussion to the national stage. And despite some right-wing hysteria about "The End Times" being upon us, the general public appeared largely unruffled by the news; most seemed to acknowledge that there were—and always have been—gay people in the world...so what was the big deal?

. . .

Regarding my own sexual orientation, I was what you'd call a "late bloomer." I didn't come out until I was 28, after falling in love with my best friend, Pat. We'd known each other since film school, and our similar backgrounds—both coming from large Catholic families—and our shared fondness for movies, books and the great outdoors ultimately drew us together.

My parents were very supportive of the relationship, although, surprisingly, it was my mother who had a tougher time dealing with it initially. As she told me later, she'd long fantasized about the day when I'd marry and become a father, because she looked forward to spoiling my kids. Therefore, it required a great deal of soul searching for her to let this dream go.

Truth be told, as I first processed my own feelings about being gay, parenthood had also been an issue for me. I'd always loved children, and thought I'd make a good father.

However, in the brave new world of 1998, having a child was no longer out of the question if you were gay or lesbian. In fact, Pat and I were currently enrolled in weekly foster parenting classes (one of which I'd had to miss, on account of the trip), with the hopes of fostering—and then later adopting—a kid. So, as I settled in for the long flight back home, I was equally abuzz about both the strange feeling I'd gotten in Godalming...and also the prospect—so long in coming—of becoming a dad.

— — —

During the flight, I ended up following the plane's progress on the video screen embedded in the back of the seat in front of me. By the time we approached Greenland, I noticed that the light filtering into the cabin had acquired a golden hue.

Looking out the window, I was amazed to see that the sea along the coastline below was absolutely choked with icebergs, which the setting sun had turned a brilliant orange.

It was a staggeringly beautiful sight, bringing to mind a quote I once read...unsure of the exact words, but it went something like "How miniscule seem the troubles of man, when looking down from heaven."

This was appropriate, since an object similar in size and composition to one of those tiny orange specks below had sent more than 1,500 people to their deaths in 1912.

Transfixed, I stared out the frosted window until we were well inland, and the tundra below had been consumed by night.

CHAPTER THIRTEEN

AVOIDANCE BEHAVIOR

Jack, Liverpool and Farncombe, England, Nov-Dec 1911

After reading his father's letter, Jack changed his plans and opted to stay in Liverpool during the break. The contents of the letter, however, continued to gnaw at him.

Your mother and I think it's high time you were married.

Indeed!

His father went further—outlining for Jack a practical solution to his "problem." It seems the old man had taken it upon himself to arrange a marriage for him! The lucky "bride-to-be"—a young woman from town—was apparently the daughter of one of his father's friends.

Jack bristled at the notion.

"The old bastard's gone too far this time," he thought. And he had every intention of telling him so the next time he saw him.

However, Jack was in no hurry for such an encounter. He didn't respond to the letter. He figured the matter could wait until Christmas.

During what turned out to be his final *Adriatic* voyage with Benny, the situation was further complicated when a message came addressed to Jack: the Marconi Company had approved his request for transfer, and he was to report to a new vessel in Southampton after the first of the year.

Since Benny had been the one to receive the message, Jack felt an explanation was in order.

"It's nothing against you," he said, "I thought it'd be better being closer to home. My sister's sick, you see, and...."

"You don't have to explain," Benny said, "I understand." But the look in his eyes told a different story.

After the ship returned to port, a flurry of last-minute messages came in; Benny, however, was intent on leaving as quickly as possible.

"If you don't mind sending them," he said, "I've got to meet my mum."

And with that, he was gone.

"Happy holidays," Jack called after him.

By rights, he was the one who should have been peeved; after all, he had the longer train ride. But Jack couldn't find it in his heart to be sore at his old friend.

Frankly, he had other things to worry about.

. . .

As his train pulled into the Farncombe station, Jack's heart sank when he saw his father on the platform. Noticing the old man was standing even more erectly than usual, Jack steeled himself for confrontation.

He wasn't disappointed. His father got to business right away.

"Did you receive my letter?" the old man asked.

"Yes," Jack replied, suddenly finding it necessary to adjust the strap of his duffel bag.

"Why didn't you respond?"

Despite his vow to the contrary, Jack suddenly lost the will to fight. He was tired, and he felt evasiveness would serve him better at the moment. Therefore, he merely listened as his father once again listed the reasons—which he'd already out-lined in the letter—why he felt his friend's daughter would be a suitable wife.

The old man informed Jack he'd invited the girl—whose name was Kitty—and her parents to the family's Yuletide par-ty so she and Jack could have a chance to meet.

"Wonderful," Jack thought.

Luckily, the holiday—and his father's blasted party—was several days away. In the meantime, Jack was able to spend a great deal of time away from the apartment.

One afternoon he took a stroll into Godalming, taking his time to notice how much the tiny berg had changed. The Grammar School, however, was exactly as he remembered it.

As Jack gazed at the old brick building, the classroom door opened and a familiar figure stepped out and began clapping a couple of chalkboard erasers together.

Although the man's bushy mustache was graying, Jack recognized him immediately: it was the most-hated School-master—the same man whose class Jack had walked out on all those years before.

The Schoolmaster nodded in his direction, but Jack, careful to make no outward sign of recognition, turned and walked away, swinging his shoulders proudly.

"The old git," he muttered under his breath.

Continuing into town, Jack paid a surprise visit to the post office, where his former co-workers greeted him warmly. He spent an hour making the rounds and catching up with everyone. By the time he returned to the street, the electric lights were already on.

Passing the bank, Jack went up to the plate glass window and peered inside. He could see his old friend, George, standing behind the counter talking with a teller. When George looked up, recognition—followed by a wide grin—appeared on his face. He waved Jack inside.

An hour later, the two were holed up in a pub, catching up on each other's lives. George, a junior manager at the bank, was now married with three kids.

Several pints—and a couple hours later—George looked at his pocket watch and realized he was in trouble. As they hurriedly left the bar, George asked Jack to walk him home to help explain the situation.

George's wife was apparently waiting just inside the door. Before the two even set foot on the steps, she threw it open angrily.

Jack explained—with mixed success—that it had been his idea to keep George at the pub. In the awkward silence that followed, he apologized again and started to bid them a good night. George's wife stopped glaring at her husband long enough to recover her manners. She proceeded to invite Jack over for supper the following evening—although, as she put it, "at a more reasonable hour." Jack wasn't sure whether she was being genuine or merely courteous, but he accepted none-theless. At this point, any excuse to leave his parents' apartment was a good one.

He thanked George's wife and headed off, but not before giving George a subtle wink. For the moment, all seemed for-given. However, Jack had barely taken a few steps when George's wife started up again.

"Of all the times to do something like this," she said shril-ly, closing the door with a bang, "the week before *Christmas!*"

Jack couldn't help but notice how she'd made the holiday sound like a swear word.

Poor George, he winced, and continued on his way.

As it turned out, Jack's father was no more thrilled by his late arrival than George's wife had been. But at least—to the old man's credit—he kept his anger in check.

"Turn off the lights," he said, before heading downstairs to bed.

The next day, Jack began running low on valid reasons for leaving the apartment. However, given that he couldn't very well go to George's house without presents for the kids, he was able to stretch the dinner into two separate outings.

When evening finally arrived, Jack, bearing his small bun-dle, returned to George's place. He was relieved that the children seemed delighted by their gifts. The oldest boy was very much like his father had been at that age—quiet, serious and a stickler for rules and order.

With that distinctive shock of wavy brown hair, he looked like George too, and Jack could scarcely conceal his amuse-ment when he saw the boy ordering his younger siblings around.

The middle child—also a boy—was more outgoing than his brother and had a definite rebellious streak, so there was plenty of bickering when the parents weren't looking.

The third child was a cute, two-year-old girl with curly hair, whom George doted on.

"Spoils her rotten, he does," George's wife said to her husband as he fussed over the girl's dress.

The girl clutched Jack's present—a wooden duck figurine on wheels—throughout the meal. After dinner, the kids went upstairs to play with their toys, leaving "Uncle Jack" and their parents to discuss grown-up stuff.

As George opened another bottle of wine, he recounted for his wife the story of Jack quitting school—which, of course, sounded funnier than on the day it had happened.

"I was so proud of him for having the courage to stand up to the headmaster like that," George said.

Jack looked at him incredulously.

"Was that before or after you wouldn't speak to me for six months?" he asked indignantly.

"I did no such thing!" George said with a look of genuine surprise.

"You most certainly did!" Jack countered. "Don't you remember?"

After a moment of silence, George nodded. "Yeah, you're right," he said. "But it was probably because I was jealous you didn't have to go to school anymore, and I did."

Jack laughed, feeling absurdly pleased that George had finally owned up to it.

The rest of the evening was pleasant. Jack enjoyed spending time with George's wife, who was very nice and like her husband, seemed impressed with Jack's work. They talked about some of the places he'd visited.

At one point, George's wife admitted that, although she and George would love to travel, "with the house and kids, there's not too much money left over for frivolous adventure."

Walking back to his parents' apartment later that night, Jack couldn't help but compare his life to George's. His friend had a good job, a nice house and a wonderful family. Jack knew that, while he might want those things at some point in his life, he was perfectly content for the time being.

He also thought about what George had told him back at the pub.

"Your life," he had said, poking Jack's shoulder again and again for emphasis, "is *far more exciting* than mine."

He also thought about what George's wife had said about the couple not having the "means for frivolous adventure." In truth, Jack felt that way himself, although this would probably be inconceivable to those who spoke enviously of his ability to sail into exotic ports around the world. But Jack knew the reality; he was never truly free to break loose, since, first and foremost, he had a job to do. He longed for the day when he could go wherever he wanted, without the constraint of always having to report back to the ship.

He wanted to see the world on his own terms—to visit places like the jungles of India and the American West, places that were hundreds of miles from the nearest seaport. He'd read about Rudyard Kipling's visit to Yellowstone Park in Wyoming, and longed to see it with his own eyes. There were so many destinations to explore and Jack knew he'd barely seen a fraction of them. Settling down with a family in Farncombe, he knew, would dash those hopes forever.

But how could he possibly make his parents understand?

Jack was sure of one thing: he had to try.

When the day of the holiday party arrived, Jack's mother and sisters spent hours cooking, cleaning and decorating the Phillips home.

Jack, on the other hand, spent a lazy afternoon reading a book he'd bought in London—although, truth be told, he had trouble concentrating on the words. Across the room, his stone-faced father was engrossed in his own volume, and the silence was palpable.

When night fell, Jack finally took his bath and retreated to the bedroom to put on his uniform and a freshly laundered shirt.

Despite having little interest in the arranged marriage, he found himself getting nervous just the same.

"Must impress the girl's parents," he thought, as he straightened his tie.

At six o'clock on the nose, the doorbell rang, with a buzz that reverberated throughout the second-floor apartment.

Jack went to the window to peer out. The stoop below was well lit. He could see a handsomely dressed man and woman standing there; next to them was a girl, obviously the daughter.

He strained to get a closer look.

"That's Kitty?" he said under his breath.

CHAPTER FOURTEEN

LUCY BRIDE

Paul, West Hollywood, California, 1998-2002

Shortly after I returned from England, and before Pat and I became foster parents, my mom sent me a box of childhood mementos. (She was very thoughtful that way.)

I found it interesting poking through the stuff, which included old photographs, my first Halloween mask (I'd been a clown), and my "baby book." As anyone who's had the opportunity to flip through an old "baby book" knows, looking at those flattened keepsakes (including the obligatory tuft of dried hair—*First Haircut!*) is definitely a surreal experience.

My book, in particular, contained a couple of other finds. The first was a letter congratulating my parents on my birth. Its return address was The White House—apparently signed by JFK himself, just six months prior to his death. (I later learned that my godfather, Donald Amirault, had arranged for it. Thank you, Uncle Don!)

The second "find" was actually more of a re-discovery. It was a random scribble in the margin, on the page devoted to my first year (1963), where my mother had written: *"Paul loves the Boston Gas Tank!"*

I smiled as I read this, since it brought back a flood of childhood memories of an oft-repeated tale (told by my parents) of one of my baby "quirks." Apparently, when I was incredibly young, I'd become obsessed with an old commercial gas storage facility located about a mile from our house. Each day, I would beg and beg my parents to take me there to visit.

The object of my affection was a huge, circular gas tank, with a roof that raised or lowered, depending on the volume of gas inside. And although the tank (which was considered a landmark) appeared to be ancient—and wasn't, by any standard definition, beautiful—I would gaze at it rapturously from the car...and throw a tantrum if my parents attempted to drive away too soon.

And the story only got more embarrassing. Some years later, after my folks informed me that the Boston Gas Company had torn the "old eyesore" down, I'd apparently burst into tears—which, admittedly, was an odd reaction for an eight year old.

Following my visit to Godalming, however, I wondered whether my earlier obsession with the gas tank had been fueled by "memories" of a similar landmark in Jack's hometown.

Since the Internet was still a work-in-progress back in 1998, it ended up taking me a great deal of time to uncover the answer to that question. But I eventually discovered the Godalming Gas Works, which, although long-demolished, had once existed, and in Jack's time, boasted storage tanks that—although smaller—were virtually identical in construction to the one I'd fretted about as a kid in Massachusetts.

And while the practical part of my brain realized that the discovery of those mirroring gas tanks proved nothing—I thought it was a curious coincidence, nonetheless.

— — —

For the next couple of years, my past-life search proceeded in fits and starts only. Why? Because life intervened.

There's a saying about parenthood: "It's the toughest job you'll ever love." Boy, is that an understatement!

In the summer of 1998, just a few days before *Guinness World Records: Primetime* hit air, Pat and I became foster parents. And although we'd been hoping to receive a child under the age of four, we found we couldn't say no when presented with a smart, adorable 17-year-old who'd been in and out of group homes for the past few years.

(We had *absolutely no idea* we were jumping into the deep end of the pool, head first, but even now, we don't regret a single minute of the experience!)

The next 14 months were a complete blur; I was working on an all-consuming network show, while trying to make time for home and family. There were lots of great times (camping trips, cross-country vacations, and best of all, her high school graduation—which remains the proudest moment of my life).

But there were also some not-so-great times (basically summed up by the equation Parents + Teenagers = Conflicts)—and when our foster daughter abruptly moved out of the apartment a few months after she turned 18, Pat and I were devastated.

Our place seemed so empty after she left. In an effort to relieve the boredom, Pat spent hours in front of the TV, while I took to the Internet, attempting to dig up additional information about my presumed *Titanic*-era alter ego, Jack Phillips. However, I didn't find much.

Looking back on that time, I realize it was the beginning of what might be called a "life transition." The foster parenting agency wanted to give us another child right away, but Pat and I declined. We were still reeling from the experience, and didn't feel we could be effective. And then, as the weeks and months passed, we realized that parenting just wasn't in the cards for us.

For my part, I have no problem admitting I was afraid. The thought of investing additional years of love and devotion into another child—with no guarantee it wouldn't end the same way—was just too painful to contemplate. Frankly, I didn't believe my heart could survive a replay. And since Pat felt the same way, we closed that chapter and moved on, each dealing with the situation in our own way.

. . .

One night, while I was again searching the web, I came across a Marconi website with printed transcripts of the wireless traffic heard on the North Atlantic the night *Titanic* sank. Reading the distress messages Jack Phillips had sent—and the various responses from other ships—did little to cheer me up. In fact, it induced a crying jag.

I was aware that this was a textbook psychological response. I was grieving the loss of a loved one...and what better way to release it than to immerse myself in the monumental sadness of the *Titanic* tragedy?

A few weeks later, however, I had a much different reaction to the events of April 15, 1912, when I stumbled upon a website that actually recreated the audio of Jack's final Marconigraph transmissions. Naturally, I could only stand listening to it for a couple seconds before turning it off; the hair on the back of my neck was standing up, and I had gooseflesh that tingled from the soles of my feet to my forehead.

— — —

At some point I began to wonder: were there others out there who also felt they had an inexplicable past-life connection to the *Titanic* disaster? Assuming the tenets of reincarnation were true, I reckoned there had to be a lot of other people in my situation.

So many lives were lost in the sinking, and that number grew exponentially when you added in the families—on both sides of the Atlantic—who'd been literally torn apart by the disaster. And not to mention the 705 survivors who obviously carried the memory of that horrendous night for the rest of their lives.

I thought it might be helpful to start an anonymous Internet discussion group on the subject. Using the words "past life" and "*Titanic*," I did a quick web search; much to my surprise, I learned there already was such a group. It was called, naturally enough, *Titanic Memories*.

I was further shocked to discover that one of the moderators was a woman who called herself "Lucy Bride."

She was a 24-year-old elementary school teacher from Florida who claimed to have vivid memories of the life of Lucy Downie, a British schoolteacher who'd met and married *Titanic*'s junior Marconi Officer Harold Bride after the disaster. As past-life stories go, hers was impressive. She seemed to "remember" a great deal about Harold and Lucy's post-*Titanic* life.

I exchanged several emails with "Lucy." She made it clear she was interested in hearing my story.

"Please, please tell me what you know/remember about 'Jack,'" she wrote. "Though Lucy never met him, she heard *all* about him from Harry (severe survivor's guilt)."

She also asked me to send her a picture. She ended her email with "I look nearly identical to Lucy—*even the Bride family says so.*"

I sent back an email promising to write my story and send it to her within a week. But I wouldn't even come close to making it. I started writing that evening, but along the way, I stopped.

Nagging thoughts of self-doubt troubled me. How did my story—when you got right down to it—really compare to hers? What did I actually have? I didn't have any memories of Jack's life per se, just a strange emotional connection to him.

Sure, I'd felt déjà vu in Godalming, but couldn't that have just been wishful thinking?

Yeah, I cried at *Titanic* movies. But that was true of half the world, thanks to Kate Winslett and Leonardo DiCaprio.

As I tried putting the words to paper, I found myself struggling. After several hours, I stopped and re-read what I'd written. That was a mistake. Even the descriptions of my two *"Titanic"* flashbacks—seeing the black steel hull from water level, and experiencing the sinking on deck—seemed silly and insubstantial when viewed with a critical eye.

Getting discouraged, I once again trolled the web. Calling up Jack's photo, I had to admit I didn't look a thing like him. On the other hand, I realized that, if reincarnation were true, it would be *highly coincidental* if I did look like him. I certainly bore little resemblance to the South Sea native whom I'd seen getting speared in the leg.

But still, what would "Lucy" think if I sent her my photo? What would she make of a paunchy, middle-aged guy who merely *thought* he was Phillips, but who offered no real memories, no proof?

As I reread the page about Jack's life, I noticed his birth date was April 11, 1887. Checking the computer's calendar, I saw the date was April 11, 2002. Coincidentally, Jack's 115th birthday.

For a diversion—or to perhaps honor his memory on the anniversary of his birth—I returned once again to the website with the reprinted *Titanic* distress messages. The tears began flowing as soon as I began to read. In fact, I bawled my eyes out for several minutes.

When it was over—and I was emotionally spent—I shut down my computer and went to bed.

I was aware, however, that my over-the-top reaction begged a deeper question: why the obsession with Jack? What exactly was I trying to prove?

. . .

For several years, I'd been what might be called "a highly motivated, armchair scholar of spirituality." (Although—if I were being honest with myself—I couldn't say whether my intentions were to disprove *all* religions, or to ultimately find one I could get behind.)

As a child, my Roman Catholic faith was unshakable. Each week I looked forward to Mass, and loved the peaceful feeling I got upon entering the church, which I genuinely believed was God's house.

It wasn't until I was 15 that cracks began to appear in my belief system.

It started with Mrs. O'Connor. She was my 7th and 8th grade homeroom teacher who also taught first- and second-year French. She was lovely, smart, and extremely patient. And although physically petite, she became a lioness at the first sign of bullying in the classroom. (She had a zero-tolerance policy...long before such a thing was acknowledged, much less named.) Naturally, Mrs. O'Connor ended up going to bat for me—the class' resident chubby kid—several times, publicly calling out my name-callers and embarrassing them. For that reason alone, I'll always be grateful.

One other indelible memory I have of Mrs. O'Connor is when she took up a collection for the family of another student who'd lost her home in a tragic nighttime fire. I'm not sure how much the class was eventually able to scrounge up, or whether it made any real difference, but it felt good to be able do something constructive in response to a tragedy. Our classmate, who'd been rescued from the blaze by firemen, was in the hospital with burns over her face and hands. In the end, sadly, she suffered permanent facial disfigurement, and just before she returned to school, I remember Mrs. O'Connor instructing the class on how to behave in her presence—no staring or treating her differently, no bringing up the fire unless she talked about it first—in an effort to make the girl feel comfortable and safe.

To my mind, if there was a person who fully espoused Jesus' "Golden Rule," it was Mrs. O'Connor.

She was the kind of teacher who made a difference. The type you'd reach out to, years later, to say thanks for everything you taught me, and for the values you instilled in me.

But, unfortunately, I never got that chance.

During the spring of my freshman year of high school, I came home to see Mrs. O'Connor's picture splashed across the front page of our local newspaper. The first thing I learned from the article was that her name was Ruth, which I hadn't known. The second thing I learned was that she'd been murdered—at the age of 28. Apparently, the Zen-like atmosphere she'd created in our classroom was the antithesis of her actual home life.

During the previous year, she and her husband had separated, and the guy became what we would now call a stalker. One night, while she was entertaining a new boyfriend, her estranged husband showed up at her apartment. Neighbors reported hearing a female's screams, followed by gunshots. By the time police arrived, Mrs. O'Connor, her boyfriend and her husband were all dead. It was the first time I can recall seeing the words "love triangle" and "murder-suicide" in print.

It was also my first experience with the death of someone I cared for. I don't believe I cried when I heard the news...but it did shock me to the core. How could something like this happen to someone I knew to be good? For what reason would God allow this?

As a Catholic, I was taught to believe that, when a person dies, their soul goes to a kind of limbo (Purgatory) until the prayers of the faithful—imploring God on their behalf—reach a sort of tipping point, after which time the soul is admitted into heaven.

Thus, it was immediately clear what I needed to do. As Mrs. O'Connor herself taught me, action was the best response to tragedy.

The next morning, I went in early to my Catholic high school to have a talk with the resident priest. As I knew, each day began with a prayer. During homeroom, the priest—or sometimes a nun—would address the student body via the public address system, asking everyone to pray for a deceased member of the community. This was often a relative or friend of one of the students or faculty members. At other times we'd be asked to pray for the healing of a sick person—and later get updates on their recoveries. Thus, being a firm believer in the power of prayer, I knew that, after all she'd done for me, the least I could do for Mrs. O'Connor would be to ask my Catholic brothers and sisters to help pave the way for her to get to heaven.

That morning, as I headed to Father Steve[4]'s office, I was looking forward to seeing him as well. He wasn't just a nameless priest. Since he'd previously worked at my hometown church, even instructing my bible studies class, I knew him well. And to say I looked up to him would be an understatement.

---

[4] Not his real name.

Father Steve was young, fit, and handsome, but instead of getting married and starting a family, he'd chosen to dedicate his life to God. And with his calm voice and gentle demeanor, he was, to my mind, almost the actual embodiment of Christ. You've heard the expression, "He's got a light from within?" That was Father Steve. Faith just oozed off of him.

He smiled in greeting as I entered his office. However, once I shared with him my request, his demeanor abruptly changed. "Well, I hardly think *that's* appropriate for our school," he said, with a look of unmistakable scorn. "She was having an affair with someone who was *not* her husband...."

Frankly, I was stunned. Never in a million years had I expected this reaction. I stammered for a few moments trying to come up with a response. The best I could do was, "But she was *a good person...*."

"Don't worry, Paul," Father Steve said at last, with a distinct air of smugness. "The nuns and I will pray for her soul...privately, of course." Then he gave me a wink and the meeting was over.

In a daze, I walked to my homeroom...feeling just like Dorothy must have felt after peeping behind that velvet curtain in Oz.

I was barely seated when the morning prayer came on over the P.A. system. I don't recall what was said, but it was along the lines of—"Today we ask everyone to remember Sister Theresa's 87-year-old Aunt Millie, who went to the hospital last night for blah blah blah...."

Then the voice on the loudspeaker faded away, marking the beginning of another school day. But for me, it was anything but ordinary. My previously held belief that the Roman Catholic clergy were superhuman, that they somehow possessed a direct, "mystical connection" to the heart and mind of God, was sorely tested. And looking back, that moment became the catalyst for another profound realization: that the job of ascertaining the "Ultimate Truth" of this world was something I'd need to discover for myself.

– – –

However, in the spring of 2002, I had to admit I was no closer to locating that truth. In the aftermath of that tearful night at the computer, I had the sneaking suspicion that my "past-life" connection to Jack and the *Titanic* was the result of wishful thinking, and as far as I could see, devoting any more energy to the "search" would be a waste of time.

For the next several months, I pretty much put the entire business away.

But then, one day in January of 2003, while visiting a museum in Florida, I saw a photo that literally sent shivers down my spine. The thing was, the guy in the picture looked a lot like me. Eerily so.

But it certainly couldn't have been, because the photo was taken fifty years before I was even born.

And one more thing...it was taken in *Titanic*'s Marconi Room.

CHAPTER FIFTEEN

MGY

Jack, Southampton, England, and Belfast, Ireland, January-April, 1912

Shortly after the New Year, Jack reported back to Southampton to assume the post of second Marconi operator aboard the *RMS Oceanic*. As far as he was concerned, the question about his impending "marriage" had now been settled—although he knew others back home shared a different view.

As he signed onto the ship, Jack hoped his new first Marconi officer would be decent, unlike Benny. He didn't feel he could personally handle any more rancor at the moment. But he found himself pleasantly surprised: he and his boss got along famously right away—and as a result, he met several of the man's friends among the ship's crew.

One of them, a junior officer named Jim Moody, was the same age as Jack, and the two quickly became pals. Jack enjoyed spending time—and matching wits—with Jim, whom he felt was his equal in terms of overall cleverness. (And although it's not something he was consciously aware of, the fact that Jim was good looking certainly added to Jack's attraction.)

Jim had only recently made the jump to passenger steamers, having spent the bulk of his career working on freighters bound for South America. Thus, as he explained to Jack, he was "eternally grateful."

"Give it a few months," the more jaded Jack told him, "and you'll be sick of it like the rest of us."

"We'll see," Jim said, flashing his ever-present smile.

The two men's coinciding schedules meant they often shared meals in the crew dining room. And after the ship arrived in New York, they explored the city together on their days off.

With a newfound friend helping pass the time, Jack made three idyllic roundtrips aboard *Oceanic*, and just as he was looking forward to his fourth, another worker's strike dashed those plans.

On March 17th, the British coal workers walked off the job. Without them, fuel could not be delivered to the ship. To Jack's dismay, the *Oceanic*'s subsequent voyage was cancelled. Apparently, all existing stores of coal on White Star ships were being confiscated so the company's newest liner could make its much-anticipated maiden voyage the following month.

"Those bloody Irish bastards!" Jack exclaimed indignantly on hearing the news. "Naturally they'd strike on St. Patrick's Day!"

To add to Jack's misery, the weather in Southampton was abominable. It was raining cats and dogs, as his aunt used to say, and Jack and Jim were forced to remain holed up in the mariner's house where they'd been staying between voyages.

Jim, who'd been working virtually non-stop since the previous summer, decided the time was right to ask for some time off. He remained in good spirits as he waited to see if his request would be approved.

Unfortunately, Jim's holiday wouldn't materialize. A telegram arrived instructing him to report to Belfast at the end of the month to assume junior officer duties aboard the much-heralded *RMS Titanic*. Apparently, he would be accompanying the ship during its sea trials, and sail with it to New York on its maiden voyage.

"You lucky dog," Jack exclaimed when Jim shared with him the news.

The next day, Jack received some news of his own: he was also joining *Titanic*. And the best part was the post came with a promotion. He would, at long last, be joining the ranks of First Marconi Officers.

One major difference between Jack's assignment and Jim's was that Jack would have to report to Belfast immediately. The *Titanic*, which was in the final stages of being outfitted, still needed to have the Marconi equipment installed, and Jack was to receive special training in that regard.

Now it was Jim's turn to be jealous.

"You lucky bastard," he said with a laugh, clearly envious that Jack would be receiving an additional week's wages. With his plans for an extended holiday dashed, Jim would have preferred to be working, instead of kicking around soggy Southampton.

"See you in Belfast," Jack said lightly, and went to his room to pack.

That afternoon, he took the train to Liverpool, and boarded a steamer for Ireland. Since the weather had now cleared, he spent most of his waking moments on the ship's deck. Although there was a definite nip to the air, Jack didn't mind. He loved the freedom of being an ordinary ship's passenger.

Darkness had fallen by the time the steamer pulled up to the dock in Belfast. While cruising up the River Lagan, Jack got his first glimpse of *Titanic*. Its imposing hull would have been hard to miss, even had the ferry not steamed directly beneath its shadow as it passed.

Although many of its portholes were dark, *Titanic*'s upper stories were well illuminated. Jack noticed a couple of workers taking a smoke break on the Boat Deck high above.

After disembarking the ferry, Jack spent the night at a local hotel and the next morning, he left before sunrise to report to the Harland & Wolff shipyard across the river. Even at this hour, the streets were jammed with men who, like Jack, were making their way to work.

At the gates, a couple of bored guards waved them all through.

Most of the men were heading to an enormous iron, cage-like structure called a gantry—where Jack could see the outline of another steamer under construction. Jack had never seen the innards of a ship before, especially from the level of its keel. It was an extraordinary sight.

Although most of the workers had detoured at the gantry, several of them, like Jack, were continuing upriver where, as Jack could plainly see, *Titanic* was anchored.

"Let's see what this tub looks like in daylight," he thought, as the ship continued to grow in size and stature.

Titanic didn't disappoint. The giant steamer, with bow pointing directly toward him, glistened in the morning sun.

The area around the dock was a beehive of activity, with dozens of workers scurrying about. Jack watched as an assortment of bed frames, tables, and vanities were carted aboard the ship.

After pausing for a moment to take in the sight, Jack reported to the office of the outfitting crew, which was located inside a warehouse on the port side of the ship. Once he signed in and received his identification papers, he was told the Marconi Room was located on the Boat Deck aft of the bridge.

"Has the equipment arrived?" he asked the harried desk clerk. "Or do you know?"

"I'm not sure," the man replied. "Why don't you go an' have a look about, and if it's not there, come back and we'll sort it out."

Jack left the office and, dodging various workers, carefully made his way to the gangway. The smell of fresh paint assailed his nostrils as soon as he approached the ship. He almost gagged.

"Hope there's enough time to air this out," he thought, "or the passengers won't be happy."

Jack stepped through the hatchway on to E deck. Since the entrance was intended for crew, it was simple and utilitarian. Jack could hear the sound of distant hammering as he began making his way forward along the main hallway, which, despite some twists and turns, appeared to be heading in the right direction.

Near the far end of the corridor, Jack came upon an opulent set of stairs decorated with carved wood. He walked up

one deck, and found himself at the foot of an even more impressive staircase, which was multi-storied, and seemed to
soar dozens of feet into the air. Presuming that this "First
Class" staircase would eventually lead him to the Boat Deck,
Jack began to climb, all the while marveling at the intricate
moldings, fittings and decorations he found on each level.
Since this part of the ship was free of workers, things were
quiet, and Jack's footfalls echoed loudly with each step.

When he finally got to the top, he went outside to the Boat
Deck.

It was a perfect day—the sky above dotted with puffy
clouds. Jack walked over to the railing to take in the view.
Given that he was now hundreds of feet above the ground, the
shipyard and the Belfast skyline across the river spread out
before him like a panorama.

Naturally, the construction gantry dominated the view, and
Jack spent a few minutes studying the caged ship. Even from
this distance, he could see an army of tiny men working on its
steel frame.

"Time to get back to work," he said softly.

He found his lodgings in the rear of the boathouse easily
enough; there was a hand-scrawled note reading "Marconi
Room" taped to the suite's outer door.

Inside, the main compartment was empty, except for some
built-in shelving, a telephone, and a couple of brass pipes
along the far wall.

Opening the door to his left, Jack discovered a small bedroom containing bunks and a large wardrobe. The furniture
took up most of the floor space.

Directly across from the bunkroom was the "Silence Cabin," where the machinery required to run the wireless would

be housed. Peeking inside, Jack noted this room too was empty. The equipment had obviously not been delivered.

At that moment, Jack became aware of a loud clanking sound. Apparently, the ship's elevator shaft was located directly behind the Marconi Room, and someone was clearly using one of the lifts at the moment.

Glancing about the room once again, Jack couldn't help but feel disappointed. He wasn't used to being hidden away like this. On most ships, Marconi Rooms were outside on the Boat Deck, giving officers easy access to a breath of fresh air, or as was more often the case, a quick cigarette.

"We don't even have a window," Jack thought glumly.

Looking up, however, he realized he was wrong; pale morning light was streaming in from a skylight. Through the window's multi-pane glass, Jack could see the top third of *Titanic*'s giant forward funnel, black with an orange stripe, looming over him.

Trying to get a better view, he stepped back. The funnel appeared to move suddenly, as if it were about to topple over. Jack flinched and backed up farther. Strangely, the phenomenon repeated. He realized that the perceived movement was actually an optical illusion, created by the skylight's double panes of glass.

"That's disconcerting," Jack thought, as his heart rate slowly returned to normal.

Lowering his eyes, he focused on the brass tubes in the corner of the room. These were pneumatic tubes, designed to deliver cylindrical metal canisters containing passenger messages.

"No more running messages back and forth to the Purser's Office," he thought.

This was why, on a ship significantly larger than *Maureta-nia*, only two Marconi officers would be required per voyage. The pneumatic technology had eliminated the need for a third officer. But a third officer still had other duties in the Marconi Room, and Jack knew that without him, he and the second operator would be kept busy.

Speaking of seconds, Jack thought, where was Bride?

The boy should be here by now. And the Marconi technician, too. Jack wondered if he'd been given the wrong information.

He pulled out his telegram and double-checked it. No, he was right. He was supposed to be here today. But where the hell was everyone else?

Jack returned to the warehouse and discovered the clerk he'd spoken to earlier was even more harried than before. Several people were now queued up waiting to speak with him. Jack took his place in line. A few minutes later, a voice called out from behind:

"Jack Phillips?"

Jack turned to see a young boy in a Marconi uniform toting a duffel bag.

"Harold Bride," the boy said, proffering his hand. "Nice to meet you. Sorry I'm late, I just got in this morning, and had to walk from the dock."

Jack told him that wasn't a problem, since the equipment, apparently, had yet to arrive.

"Have you seen our quarters?" the boy asked. "What are they like?"

Jack described the Marconi suite, and Harold asked several more questions about the ship.

The boy is very eager, Jack mused. He had the nagging feeling that Bride reminded him of someone, but couldn't remember whom.

As they waited, Bride peppered Jack with questions about his previous postings, and then launched into a blow-by-blow account of the ships he himself had worked on.

As the boy yammered on, Jack realized who it was Bride reminded him of—at least, personality wise: Benny.

"But I'll try not to hold that against him," Jack thought, as he finally stepped up to the desk to speak with the clerk.

As it turned out, the Marconi equipment had not been delivered, and would not arrive until the following day. A telegram to that effect—addressed to Jack—was buried on the clerk's desk, although it wouldn't be discovered until later.

In the meantime, at the clerk's suggestion, Jack and Harold spent a great deal of time combing through the warehouse searching for the missing crates.

When they finally gave up and returned to the desk, Jack asked the clerk for the location of the nearest post office so he could send a cable to the company to advise them of the missing equipment. This triggered the clerk's memory, and, with several apologies, he finally produced the missing telegram.

The message informed Jack that the Marconi technician, along with the equipment, would be arriving the following morning, and that he and Bride were to meet the technician at the dock.

With little else left to do, Jack and Harold spent an hour or so touring and familiarizing themselves with the ship, before walking back to the hotel.

The next morning, they met the technician and helped arrange for the transportation of the heavy crates.

Since *Titanic*'s Marconi Room was owned by Marconi—
and rented to the White Star Line—it was not the responsibility of Harland & Wolff employees to haul the equipment
aboard ship. This backbreaking work, Jack discovered, fell to
him, Bride and the company technician, although he was
grateful that at least they wouldn't have to lug the crates up
stairs. They could use a First Class elevator for that.

At one point, Jack became careless and, while stepping
from the lift, allowed a crate to rub against the cage, leaving a
long scratch in the black paint. Since no one else saw it, Jack
said nothing; although later, before the ship left Belfast, he
smiled when he noticed someone had apparently discovered
the nick and repainted it.

The suite took the better part of two days to outfit. Like all
Marconi Rooms, the receiving equipment was set up in the
main compartment, while the sending equipment was installed
in the Silence Cabin. As Jack well knew, the systems had to
be separate, or else interference from the sending equipment
would make the receiving equipment inoperable.

Both he and Bride enjoyed learning how to put everything
together—it went without saying this was a new skill that
would make them more valuable in the company's eyes.

After the installation was complete—and the technician
steaming back to England—Jack and Bride checked out of
their hotel and returned to the ship with their duffel bags.
They would now be residing on *Titanic* full time.

During their first night, Jack was kept awake by the annoying clank of the First Class elevators. The racket didn't appear
to disturb Harold, who could be heard snoring away in the
bunk below. Jack decided, once the voyage got underway, to

set a work schedule that would allow him to sleep while the infernal things were shut down for the night.

"That'll solve the problem," Jack thought, as he turned over and covered his head with the pillow.

The next morning, several of the ship's officers and crew-members—including Jim Moody—began to arrive. Captain Edward J. Smith, however, was not among them. The legendary White Star captain wouldn't join the ship until right before the start of sea trials.

The next couple of days were fun for Jack. Since the ship's wireless consumed so much power, it could not be tested properly until more of the ship's boilers were lit. Thus, there wasn't much to do except organize the office.

In the evenings, Jack, Harold and Jim—along with the rest of the crew—ate dinner in the First Class dining room. The men laughed and told stories and thoroughly enjoyed the luxuriousness of their surroundings. They knew the cushy arrangement would end once passengers were aboard. At that time, the officers would take their meals in the Crew Dining Room up on B Deck, while Jack and Bride ate with the postal workers on C Deck.

"It figures," Jack thought, upon learning of the arrangement, "second-class once again."

On the day before *Titanic* was scheduled to sail, Jack saw an army of tugs assembling off the starboard side of the ship. As he learned from Jim, the steamer was facing the wrong way and needed to be turned downriver before the start of sea trials. *Titanic*'s own powerful engines could not be used for this purpose, as they lacked precision and could cause the massive vessel to ground itself or crash into something.

The process ended up taking hours, as the ship was pulled, at dead weight, to the center of the river and slowly rotated, the bow resembling, to Jack's mind, the creeping shadow of a sundial moving from noon to six.

That evening, most of the crewmembers left to enjoy their last night in port. Jack and Harold decided to stay on board with Jim and the other officers. However, when his superiors had retired to their rooms, Jim offered to give Jack and Harold a tour of some of the more exclusive areas of the ship. They agreed to go right away.

For Jack, the highlight was the Turkish Bath down on F-Deck. He was particularly impressed with the ornate, Arabian-style tile covering its walls.

But the ship's pool across the hall, on the other hand, gave him the willies. The idea of swimming in a small dark room in the bowels of the vessel was a strange and unsettling concept. He wasn't sure how popular it would be with the passengers, either.

Bride, however, took the occasion of visiting the pool to begin a lengthy dissertation on the pros and cons of the various strokes used by swimmers.

Jack's annoyance with him was growing. The boy was apparently fast at the key—not quite up to Jack's speed, but fast enough, especially given his age, 22, and level of experience. But the problem was he was even faster with the tongue. He seemed to feel the need to fill every second with some sort of joke, comment, or observation, as if silence itself were a frightening beast that could only be slain by chatter. Jack, who could be as gregarious as the next man, knew there was a time and a place for everything; however, this was a lesson, unfortunately, his second Marconi officer had yet to learn.

"Let's go to town for a pint," Jack said, interrupting Harold's backstroke discussion mid-stream.

Jim was receptive to the idea, and soon the three were trudging across Queens Island Bridge. But Jack soon regretted his impetuousness.

If Bride's chatter was annoying when he was sober, then, with a few pints under his belt, he became positively unbearable. There wouldn't be a moment's peace until he was knocked out in his bunk a couple hours later. Jack spent the intervening time thinking up clever ways of ditching Harold in the future.

"Don't want to be anywhere near him when we get to New York," he thought.

The next morning, Jack awoke before dawn. After dressing and shaving in the officers' lavatory across the hall from the Marconi Room, he left to find some breakfast. When he returned thirty minutes later, Bride was still asleep.

"Get up, Harold," he said crossly. "We sail in an hour."

Bride, apparently, flew directly from his bed into his clothes, because he joined Jack in the Marconi Room just moments later. But the haste, it turned out, was for naught. The weather had turned, and the daylight coming through the skylight was a dull gray.

When they stepped outside to smoke, they could barely get their cigarettes lit on account of the wind. Jack bummed a light from Moody, who, along with the other officers, were smoking and looking doubtfully down at the river. The wind had created a noticeable chop in the brown water, and the tugboats that had once again pulled up were being tossed around.

By captain's orders, the launch was eventually scrubbed for the day.

Early the next morning, the drill was repeated. The ship was scheduled to depart at 6 a.m., so Jack was up well before four. Once again, however, it took some prodding to extricate Harold from his bunk. Jack saw the morning sunlight streaming in through the skylight, and knew there'd be no further reprieves.

They were underway shortly. Jack and Harold watched the operation from the deck as the tugboats towed the ship to the open sea. Once the tugs fell back, *Titanic*'s engines rumbled to life, and soon the giant ship was powering under its own steam.

While the captain began maneuvering the vessel through the Irish Sea, Jack and Harold fired up the transformer and spent the day checking the wireless' range. Jack remained at the key sending test messages, while Harold documented everything in the logbook.

When Marconi land stations in Egypt, Africa and the Canary Islands began flashing back their responses, Jack was frankly astonished.

The old tub's wireless was powerful indeed.

Unfortunately, though, Jack and Harold couldn't get the battery-powered, back-up Marconigraph to work. When they tried setting it up, they discovered it was missing the cables required to patch it to the battery pack. And since the cables on the ship's main set were different, they couldn't be used.

Jack sent a message to Marconi House in London notifying them of the problem, and shortly thereafter received a reply telling him that the situation would be rectified when the ship docked in Southampton.

During the next several hours, Jack spent a great deal of time sending Marconigrams for one of the White Star officials on board. The man, Harold Sanderson, brought the slips of paper to the Marconi Room himself. Most of them appeared to be business-related, although some, clearly, were not.

"It's his ship," Jack reasoned, "so the man can do what he wants."

At one point, Bride, after reading one of Sanderson's messages, made a joke about its contents. Jack looked at him sternly. Summoning up his most professorial voice, he began lecturing Harold on the privacy of Marconigrams. Naturally, he cribbed the speech almost word for word from the one he himself had received all those years before.

Jack was struck by the difference between Bride's reaction to the lecture and his own; he had sulked when the first officer called him on the carpet, despite the fact that he knew he had it coming. Harold, however, took the criticism in stride. He offered up a short "sorry" and proceeded to change the subject.

Once the sea trials had concluded, *Titanic* returned to Belfast. By this time, it was dark. After some of the more prominent passengers—including Sanderson—disembarked, the ship was once again rotated in the river by tugs, and set off again, this time for England. The maiden voyage was now just over a week away.

The 600-mile trip took a little over a day. Since Jack didn't have a lot of official business to attend to, he spent much of the voyage on deck, pretending to be an ordinary ship's passenger. When *Titanic* approached the Isle of Wight the following afternoon, he got a glimpse of the Needles Lighthouse, and behind it, the familiar line of rock formations stretching back to the cliffs.

With great interest, he spent a few moments studying the top of the nearby cliffs, looking in vain for the hotel his family had visited during that long ago summer. He saw no sign of it. Then he remembered Marconi telling him it had burned down. Apparently, though, it hadn't been rebuilt.

A few minutes later, when the ship passed the town of Freshwater, Jack could see that the beachfront hotel where his family had stayed, was still there. As he lit another cigarette, Jack reminisced about that long ago vacation. He vividly remembered the sight of the ghostly white ships passing off shore while he played on the beach.

"It's funny how things turn out," he thought.

It was almost midnight by the time the tugs maneuvered the steamer into the dock at Southampton.

After catching a few hours' sleep, Jack and Harold dressed and packed their duffels. Since the 24-hour delay in Belfast had put the crew behind schedule, Jim and the rest of the officers would have to work straight through until the ship departed the following Wednesday. But the Marconi men, on the other hand, wouldn't have to report back until Tuesday evening.

Before they disembarked, Harold asked Jack what his plans for the break were. Surmising Bride's next question might be to ask if he could tag along, Jack told him he planned on visiting the Isle of Wight to spend some time with his sister. This wasn't true, but as lies go, it was convenient.

In the end, Jack made the story he told Harold at least partially true. Although Elsie wouldn't be joining him, he decided to visit the Isle by himself. And he thoroughly enjoyed spending a few quiet hours alone.

Jack ended up spending the rest of the break in London, catching up with some old friends from Marconi School. (As it turned out, several of them were in town thanks to the ongoing coal strike, which had idled their ships.) The men surprised him with an early 25th Birthday celebration. His actual birthday—April 11th—wouldn't take place 'til the following Thursday when he was at sea.

Jack had a good time—too good, actually, and awoke on Easter Sunday with a headache. Nevertheless, he pulled himself together for services at St. Paul's Cathedral.

On Tuesday morning, he took the train back to Southampton, arriving at the White Star Dock in the late afternoon. Harold was not there. However, by this time, the missing cables for the back-up Marconigraph had been delivered. Jack tested the set—which now worked—and had a low-key dinner with Moody and the other officers. And although he went to bed early, the noisy elevators kept him awake for several hours. He'd just fallen asleep when Harold arrived, stumbling around in the darkened bunkroom.

"Sorry," he said, after bumping into the edge of the bunk.

"What time is it?" Jack asked.

"Almost midnight," Harold said.

"We get up at four," Jack said, and promptly fell back to sleep.

The next morning, Bride shook him awake.

"What time is it?" he asked groggily.

"Four," Harold said, before leaving the room to wash up.

As he rubbed the sleep from his eyes, Jack was pleased to see that Harold became professional during actual voyages.

The weather outside was perfect as he and Bride made their way below deck for breakfast. The postal dining room on

C deck was a Spartan affair. Food and tea were laid out on a small table near the door, and it was first come, first served.

While wolfing down eggs and bangers, Jack looked around the table at the rest of the postmen. No one said a word as they ate. One man, who was thin and gangly with a moustache that was much too big for his face, kept his nose in his book the entire time.

"This is a cheery lot," Harold said quietly in Jack's ear.

"Like a bloody funeral."

Jack smirked as he sipped his tea. "The kid's okay," he thought.

After breakfast, Jack and Harold tested the hydraulic tubes. Several messages were exchanged with the Purser's Office three decks below. Before sending the first cylinder, Jack scrawled, "What's for dinner?" on a slip of paper and popped it inside. He pressed the button and the cylinder disappeared with a whoosh. A minute later, there was another whoosh—followed by a thunk—and the cylinder reappeared in the other tube. When Jack opened the container, he howled with laughter.

"Your Aunt Mildred," was the reply.

"That McElroy's a sick bastard," Jack grinned, and quickly jotted down a response: "What are you having? Your Uncle Peter?"

Jack showed Harold the message before he sent it, and the boy laughed, but suggested Jack change "Your Uncle Peter" to "Your Uncle's Peter."

Jack declined to revise it, saying McElroy wasn't thick, and would obviously get the inference.

He was right. McElroy's response came swiftly, setting off a volley of increasingly off-color messages, until the Purser three decks down finally surrendered.

"Enough. Enough."

Jack grinned. It was obvious the machinery was working.

It was a good thing too, because, just as soon as the passengers were allowed to board the ship, messages began dropping from the brass tube...sometimes two or three at a time.

"What's McElroy doing down there?" Jack thought. "Saving them up, so he can bombard us all at once?

But despite the annoyance, he was genuinely happy to get back to work.

However, shortly after the ship's noon departure, something went wrong. Without warning, *Titanic*'s booming horn began sounding.

Jack started in his chair, then jumped once again when the horn was followed by a second, more insistent blast. The boom was answered by a different ship's horn. Soon another joined the fray.

"What could possibly be the matter now?" he wondered. "We've barely left the dock!"

The ship shuddered, and Jack felt its momentum begin to slow. He turned and exchanged glances with Harold, who sat at the table beside him.

"Why don't you go see what's happening," he said.

The boy left eagerly, his footfalls trailing down the hallway, as the cacophony of horns continued. Moments later—or so it seemed to Jack—the sound of hurried footsteps returned. Bride burst back into the room, shouting excitedly.

"There's another steamer—I think we're gonna hit!"

"What?" Jack exclaimed incredulously.

He jumped up and ran outside to see for himself. And indeed, just off the port side of the ship, another large steamer was coming directly toward them.

However, it wasn't the ship's bow that was aiming to hit them broadsides—it was its stern. The ship seemed to be backing into them at an odd angle.

As Jack later learned, the wash from his own mammoth vessel had snapped the other steamer's moorings, causing it to swing out from the dock like a pendulum, aft end first.

In order to avoid a collision, the captain was apparently reversing his engines—however, it didn't appear to be doing much good.

The steamer continued swinging inexorably toward them. It was so close now Jack could read the passenger information signs on its decks. But he still hoped a crash could be averted.

Jack knew if the voyage were cancelled, he'd have no choice but to return home. Over the past few months, he'd spent a great deal of money on food and lodging between crossings, all to avoid facing his father. Until now, his plan had worked.

But his funds were getting low, and he knew he couldn't keep it up forever.

And although he also knew it was impossible for a man, through sheer force of willpower, to move tons of steel with his mind, Jack attempted to do so anyway.

"Get away from there, you old tub," he muttered under his breath, "C'mon!"

But he had no idea he should actually be praying for a crash instead.

CHAPTER SIXTEEN

"OH MY GOD, IT'S TRUE!"

Paul, Orlando, Florida & West Hollywood, January 2003

Having a birthday just after New Years can be a bummer, coming so close, as it does, to the Christmas holiday. Consequently, I never made a big deal about mine. However, for the occasion of my 40th birthday, which would take place on January 3, 2003, I wanted to do something special.

Pat and I planned a trip to Walt Disney World in Florida to celebrate. To my surprise and delight, my parents and several of my siblings—and their families—decided to join us.

Shortly after we arrived, I discovered Orlando had a permanent *Titanic* museum. I naturally added it to my "To Do" list.

On New Year's Day, I finally carved out some time to go. Pat begged off, saying he wanted to hang out by the pool. I couldn't really blame him. Over the years, he'd certainly taken in his share of *Titanic* exhibits.

My parents and my 14-year-old nephew Brad accompanied me. Truth be told, I wasn't expecting much; from experience I'd learned it was better to be surprised than disappointed.

However, the exhibit was impressive from the first minute. In the ticket office, they had one of the wooden nameplates from a *Titanic* lifeboat. Kept under glass, it read simply "*SS Titanic*." I hadn't realized any of these had survived. Reaching for my camera, I realized I'd left it back at the hotel. Thankfully though, Brad had his, and he agreed to take a bunch of snaps for me.

The main exhibit hall contained mostly survivor memorabilia. There were several pieces of jewelry Denver socialite Molly Brown had been wearing on the night of the sinking. (*Titanic* fans will recognize Molly as the character played so memorably by Kathy Bates in the movie.)

Looking around the room, I noticed the walls were covered with large black-and-white blow-ups of old photographs. I'd seen most them before—they were mainly from the Father Browne Collection. However, given the size and clarity of these prints, it was like seeing them all for the first time.

My eyes were drawn to a picture in the corner. According to its placard, the photo had been taken in *Titanic*'s Marconi Room.

"That's funny," I remember thinking. "Why hadn't I seen it before?"

I focused my attention on the man sitting at the wireless. He had his back to the camera—either unaware or unconcerned about the fact that a photo was being taken. As I stared at the photo, my mind boggled, and my heart began to pound.

The man sitting at the wireless was *me*.

He had the same posture; the same slight stoop of his shoulders as he worked; the same body language. Hell, he even had the same bald spot on the back of his head. It was identical. He looked *exactly* like I did from behind. Or I should say, like I used to look—back in my twenties, when I was thinner, before the onset of middle-age spread. I kept staring at the photo—wishing it could move. If the man sitting at the desk would just turn around—I knew—he'd have my face.

This was a curious reaction, which begged the question: how can the concept of self-recognition be explained? Most of us don't spend a great deal of time looking at ourselves from behind. It happens, say when we're at the barbershop or hairdressers and are given a mirror to check the back of a haircut. But even so, when most people are shown a photo of themselves from behind, recognition will no doubt set in. No time is spent wondering, "Who is that person? Could that be me?" Something primal kicks in, and you know. You just know.

That's how I felt looking at the picture. I felt like I was being exposed.

I don't recall how long I stood there gaping, but it could easily have been several minutes. It seemed to take forever for the implications of what I was seeing to sink in.

Once it had, I remember saying to myself, "Oh my God, it's true. *It really is true!*"

Finally, I looked up and, seeing Brad across the room, motioned for him to come over.

"Do me a favor," I asked when he got within earshot. "Would you take a picture of that photo for me?"

"Which one?" he asked.

"That one," I pointed. He took it quickly.

Brad was my godson. He knew I was a *Titanic* buff; however, I'd never told him about my supposed past-life connection to the disaster. I guess I hadn't wanted him to think his "cool" uncle from California was actually a nut case.

Trying my best to sound casual, I asked, "Does that guy in the picture look like anyone you know?"

Without missing a beat, he said, "Yeah, it looks like you."

I then told him I'd always felt a connection to the ship, and that I'd come to believe I'd actually been one of *Titanic*'s wireless officers in a previous life. He looked at me without a hint of judgment, a smile breaking over his face.

"Cool!" he said.

My parents soon wandered over. I asked my mom the same question, and her answer was identical, although, after I'd shared with her the gist of my story, she looked at the photo again and amended her response.

"Actually," she said, "you have wider shoulders than he does."

While poking around in the gift shop outside the exhibit hall, I noticed some copies of the book *Father Browne's Titanic Album,* which I'd purchased years earlier. Quickly thumbing through it, I came across the Marconi Room photo. I realized I had seen it before—however, since it was a double-exposure, it had been impossible to see the person at the wireless with any sort of clarity. Father Browne had apparently forgotten to advance the film between shots, so, in the final photo, two images can be seen, one atop the other. I could only presume the curators of the exhibit had used digital technology to remove the ghost of the second image, which allowed the details of the first to emerge.

Pat was bummed he'd missed the excitement. Because Brad's camera was actually a digital video camera that also took stills, he wasn't able to show us the photo in-camera. However, he promised to download it to his computer when he got home and email it.

Brad was as good as his word, and I was able to print out the photo as soon as I received it. Looking at it again—this time from the comfort of my California apartment—I was pleased to see the resemblance was still there. It was *me* sitting in that chair.

I went to show Pat. I knew it would have been pointless to say, "Now be honest, tell me what you really think." Pat was frankly incapable of doing anything else.

His typically succinct comment said everything.

"Wow."

A few days after returning from Florida, I started a new job. I was a show producer on one of those competition reality shows America couldn't seem to get enough of. It was a dismal experience. I found myself working around the clock—literally—for several weeks.

During that time, however, something else occurred that convinced me I needed to deal will my *"Titanic Memories."*

Oddly enough, it happened at a war protest.

While I was miserable and crazed from overwork at the reality show, America seemed to go crazy as well.

Our president, George W. Bush, was about to unleash a war on Iraq, and to my mind, the idea of a "pre-emptive" strike on a foreign nation went against our history, and even our Constitution.

Personally, I'd had some experience with war. When I was six, my father had been shipped off to Viet Nam, leaving behind a wife and five children. Luckily for us, my dad eventually came back. However, hundreds of thousands of other American soldiers weren't so lucky.

Consequently, I came to see wars as bad—especially ones in which the U.S. interceded militarily in far-off countries where we had no business. As I grew to adulthood, I thought most Americans had learned this lesson about our mistake in Viet Nam. But apparently, this wasn't the case.

I decided to exercise my First Amendment right and attend a protest march in downtown Los Angeles. Pat came with me.

We'd barely arrived when a reporter from the *Los Angeles Times* approached us for an interview. His subsequent article, *Middle-Class Dissent on Display at War Protest*, made the point that lots of ordinary citizens were on hand to protest the country's sudden—and unprovoked—march to war. In other words, it wasn't just the usual crazies who showed up at these events. That was definitely our experience. There were lots of college students, families with strollers, even retirees.

As fruitless as the protests proved to be, Pat and I ended up going to several. The last one took place the weekend before the bombs began falling on Baghdad. It was not well attended. By then, most people realized the demonstrations weren't working, and besides, it was a rainy day in L.A.

There were probably only five or six hundred there—mostly college kids—and some of the more hardcore protest types.

The sky opened up by the time the parade started, and we all got drenched as we marched down Broadway. Suddenly, from the back of the line, a group of protesters began to scream. It was kind of like a primal scream to vent pent-up feelings of frustration and anger.

"Good for them," I thought.

The screams started a chain reaction. People around them started yelling, and pretty soon, everyone was doing it. It was kind of like the wave at a baseball game. I heard it coming toward me, like the roar of an approaching freight train, getting louder and louder.

Soon, screaming people were all around us. I looked at Pat. He started to join in. My mouth opened, but no sound came out. I was struck dumb by a wave of gooseflesh that swept my entire body.

I shivered when I surmised the cause of my reaction. I thought it possible that, long ago, in the middle of the North Atlantic, I'd heard a similar, heartbreaking sound.

My weird response to the scream fest caused my enthusiasm for the protest to ebb, and long before the march ended, Pat and I were trudging back—against traffic—to our car. I realized it was finally time for me to deal with this once and for all.

I was like the old lady in the James Cameron movie. I needed to go back to *Titanic*.

It was time for another past-life regression.

When I'd first been hypnotically regressed, I'd freaked out and snapped out of the regression the moment I'd seen the image of *Titanic*. I'd done this for several reasons, not the least of which was that I was shocked by—and frankly unprepared for—the sight. However, this time, things would be different. I'd be prepared. I would stay in trance, no matter how scary or difficult or painful the things I was seeing eventually turned out to be.

If the intervening years had taught me anything, it was that I needed to face my fears. Given my emotional attachment to the disaster, it was abundantly clear there were things locked inside my head that needed to be dealt with. And unfortunately, since my friend Janeen Weiss had moved back to Chicago, I knew I'd have to find a different—but equally reputable—hypnotherapist to work with.

However, I was getting ahead of myself. In order to approach the hypnotherapy intelligently—which I felt was crucial—I needed to come up with a plan.

After a few days of mulling it over, I realized there were two major things I needed to do before returning to hypnotherapy.

The first was to take the time necessary to write down my story—to get it all out on paper. It was best to do this upfront, while things were fresh, before the facts got clouded over—*or colored*—by additional information. At the very least, having the story in one place would be helpful if I needed to refer back to it. And the simple act of writing could prove therapeutic as well.

The second thing I needed to do was to collect everything that was presently known about Jack's life. If I'd never heard of *Titanic*—or Jack—it would have been okay for me to just jump right in with the regressions.

But since I was a lifelong *Titanic* buff who'd already spent time researching Jack's life, I'd been exposed to a certain amount of information about him—whether or not I consciously remembered it. For good or bad, that genie was out of the bottle.

However, I needed a way of quantifying that information, so I'd know if I were simply regurgitating it while under hypnosis, or if I were, in fact, coming up with new things.

Given that I'd already started a research folder on Jack, I figured this part would be easy. The fact was there just weren't many sources.

Once I'd completed those two tasks, I thought, I'd be sufficiently prepared to undergo hypnosis.

After that—presuming I was able to come up with additional memories from Jack's life—I could return to England for a more extended visit. I'd fully retrace his steps, visit the places where he had lived, worked, and been taught. For instance, I understood his elementary school was still standing.

The ultimate aim would be to find something that would concretely prove—to my own satisfaction—that the connection was real.

I was excited. I had a plan, and I looked forward to setting it in motion. Since I'd just finished work on the reality show, I decided to take a few weeks off to devote to the project.

A few days later, I had lunch with my old friend, Ruth Rivin. She and I had worked together for several years. In fact, back when we were doing *Put to the Test*, Ruth had been the first person to whom I'd confided the details of that scary vision of *Titanic*.

Thus, it was only fitting that, during our catch-up lunch, I told her about the latest developments. Ruth's reaction to the Marconi Room photo—which I'd brought along—was interesting.

After studying it for a few moments, she looked up and said, "At first, there was something there…but then it was gone."

Unfortunately, Ruth's words turned out to be prophetic.

When I got home, I went back to the computer and called up the story I'd started writing for "Lucy Bride" from the *Ti-*

tanic Memories website. It wasn't as bad as I remembered. Picking up where I'd left off, I continued plowing through it.

At one point, I took a break and went to the web to download some photos of *Titanic*. I was surprised to discover the Marconi Room photo I'd seen in Orlando was also online. "Wow," I thought again, as I looked at the pic. "The resemblance is just so uncanny."

Then I noticed the caption: "*Titanic*'s Junior Wireless Operator *Harold Bride.*"

"That's not right," I thought. I walked over to my bookshelf and pulled out my copy of *Father Browne's Titanic Album*. Flipping through it, my heart sank as I read the handwritten caption beneath the picture: *"In the Marconi Room. Mr. Harold Bride, afterward saved, sitting at the table."*

Next to the Marconi Room photo was another picture, apparently taken by Father Browne as well. It showed two Marconi officers, one of whom was clearly Jack. Its caption read: *"Mr. Jack Phillips (on left), who was lost on the Titanic, taken shortly before his transfer from the Adriatic."*

Stunned, I closed the book, as realization slowly sank in. If Father Browne had photographed Jack during his posting aboard the *Adriatic*, it seemed unlikely the priest would have subsequently confused him with Bride when they later met aboard *Titanic*; in fact, logic would even suggest that the sole reason for Father Browne's visit to *Titanic*'s wireless room was because Jack—whom he'd previously met—had invited him...which certainly meant the priest would have known who was working the Marconigraph when he took his photo.

I had to face it. I was wrong. About the picture, and—quite possibly—about everything else.

Dammit! I must be going crazy!

CHAPTER SEVENTEEN

"MISS WHAT'S-HER-NAME"

Jack, North Atlantic, April 10-13, 1912

As Jack stood watching, barely breathing, the stern of the *SS City of New York* eventually swept past *Titanic*'s hull, with only a couple of feet to spare.

"'Twas a close one," he whistled, as he headed back to the Marconi Room.

. . .

Jack couldn't have known, as historians would later point out, that the most-likely result of any low impact collision between the *Titanic* and the *City of New York* would have been a delay of just a few hours—to check the White Star liner for damage—which would have put time and distance between the ship and that rogue, drifting iceberg in the Atlantic.

So, as the vessel once again began making its way toward the open ocean, everyone aboard, including Jack, went back about their business, pleased with his or her good fortune (for having, as we might say, "dodged a bullet"), blissfully unaware that a much larger gun was now taking aim at them.

– – –

Back in the Marconi Room, Jack and Harold settled into their routine. Jack spent much of the day in front of the Marconigraph, while Harold sat beside him at his desk.

When a passenger message came in through Jack's headset, he would jot it down and hand it to Harold, who'd type it and, after transcribing the details into the logbook, place it in an envelope and send it to the Purser's Office via the pneumatic tube.

However, the tube could only be used to distribute *passenger messages*.

As per usual, weather reports and other messages involving the ship's navigation (marked by the prefix MSG) had to be hand-delivered to the bridge, a task that also fell to Harold. And messages addressed to the ship's captain had to be given to the skipper personally. Normally, this sort of thing wasn't a problem; however, since *Titanic*'s bearded and gray-haired Captain Smith was rumored to be retiring once the ship returned from New York, messages of congratulations continuously poured in for him, and Harold was kept busy hunting him down, a job that, on a ship of *Titanic*'s size, proved challenging.

"Where was he this time?" Jack asked, after the boy had taken a particularly long time delivering a message.

"Down in the Parisian Restaurant," Bride said breathlessly, plopping back into his chair.

Jack knew this was not unusual behavior for a ship's captain, who were mostly figureheads. The real work of steering belonged to the senior officers. But still, Captain Smith seemed to be more of a socializer than most.

Jack had met him just once, the night *Titanic* left Belfast. Smith had poked his head into the Marconi Room, introducing himself with a firm handshake.

"He seems like an affable old feller," Jack had thought at the time, although his impression of *Titanic*'s skipper was somewhat less charitable now, with Harold constantly running off to find him.

"That's the reason," Jack thought once again, "that a ship this large needs a *third* Marconi officer!"—especially given that dealing with messages sent to and from *Titanic* was only a part of their job.

As employees of the Marconi Company, he and Bride were required to transcribe any and all transmissions overheard by wireless, even those not specifically addressed to their ship. In such cases, if the receiving ship acknowledged receipt, nothing further needed to be done. If not, however, it was Jack's job to "keep an ear out" for the other ship, and relay the message once communication was established.

Since *Titanic* had one of the newest and most powerful Marconi sets on the ocean, and Jack could hear—and broadcast—farther than most ships, a good deal of his time was spent relaying third-party messages, especially at the start of the voyage, while *Titanic* was still in range of land stations in England, while other ships with more limited equipment weren't.

Thus, work continued to be busy well into the first evening of the voyage, especially after the ship stopped in Cherbourg,

France, where several more First Class passengers boarded. First Class passengers, Jack knew, were the only ones who could afford the steep price of sending Marconigrams, and sure enough, before they were even underway, the hydraulic tube came to life once again.

That evening, Jack took a quick dinner and settled into his first solo shift, while Harold ate and promptly went to sleep.

At a little before two, the boy reappeared, and Jack was happy to turn over the key. However, rest didn't come quickly for Jack. After he'd changed and slipped into his bunk, he spent at least an hour listening to Harold send, since the zaps from the spark-gap transmitter could easily be heard from the next room. For experienced Marconi men, Morse became an ingrained language, which the mind learned to translate automatically, whenever the familiar dots and dashes were heard. As first officer, it was Jack's job to keep an eye on Harold, making sure the boy was following procedure when he was working on his own.

After eavesdropping on Harold for a while, Jack smiled. It was clear he knew what he was doing. At this point, he was finally able to relax and fall asleep.

A few hours later, Jack awoke refreshed, had a spot of breakfast, and relieved Harold. While the boy went off to eat, Jack looked over the logbooks from the previous night. He was pleased to see everything was in order.

The morning passed uneventfully, as *Titanic* stopped in Queenstown harbor to pick up the final load of passengers.

Since Jack didn't want anyone aboard ship to make a fuss about his birthday, he said nothing about it to Harold; instead, he spent much of the day wired to the Marconigraph, taking fewer breaks than usual even, in order to intercept any birthday wishes that might possibly come through. However, Jack knew this wasn't very likely. The only person who'd send such a message would be his father...and given the events of the previous Christmas, Jack felt it best not to get his hopes too high.

Therefore, he had mixed feelings when the long day finally ended and he turned over the key once again to Harold. With Ireland behind them, *Titanic* was now steaming west across the Atlantic Ocean.

As Jack undressed in the bunkroom, he was happy no one had become the wiser about his birthday. However, on the other hand, a part of him was disappointed at the silence from Farncombe.

But he hadn't really expected anything, had he?

. . .

Back in December on Christmas Eve, during the holiday party Jack's parents had thrown for the purpose of attempting to marry him off, Jack had frankly been disappointed by the sight of his supposed "wife."

He'd seen many glamorous women during his travels, and the mousy Kitty just wasn't up to the standards he'd set for himself long before.

And yet, it wasn't just Kitty's somewhat average looks that disappointed; it was the fact that there wasn't any sort of spark between them. Jack couldn't help but compare her to Mary. While the Irish girl had not been particularly glamorous, he'd found an indescribable connection with her. He could still see the twinkle in her eyes, and the mischievous smile that transformed her freckled face.

Kitty, on the other hand, merely suffered by comparison. All evening, she had looked at him with sad-looking, doe eyes. Jack realized Kitty was most likely intimidated by the situation, as he certainly was, but he couldn't help but feel that there was something more.

And if Kitty had been reserved, her father, on the other hand, was a boisterous sort who continually kept the strained conversation alive by peppering him with questions. To Jack's annoyance, the man would then repeat his every word back to Kitty, as if the girl were so dense she hadn't heard them the first time.

Also, Jack couldn't help but notice the many glances and nods Mr. Bex kept giving his father...and worse, his old man's nods, glances, and *smiles* in return.

Jack knew he must remain a gentleman. Therefore, he kept reaching for the wine.

At one point during dinner, after the conversation had died once again, Ethel reinvigorated it by asking Kitty about her needlepoint. Kitty seemed to come alive at this, and Jack knew there was a problem if Ethel had more in common with his supposed "wife" than he did.

Once the Bexes left, Jack had quarreled with his father, saying that, although Kitty seemed like "a fine young lady," she was far too quiet for him. He pointed out that Mr. Bex had done all the talking.

"Well, take her to supper," his father said, "just the two of you...and see if she opens up." Although Jack remained un-convinced, he finally agreed to the date, if only to shut the old man up.

Two nights later, Jack called at Kitty's house. Once again, Mr. Bex was solicitous, treating him like a dear, old friend.

Jack was frankly grateful to Kitty who, a few moments later, came rushing down the stairs and gave her father a peck on the check.

"Hello," she said, smiling shyly at Jack, once again refusing to meet his eyes.

"Well, let's be off, shall we?" he said.

Mr. Bex gave Jack a pat on the back, and a conspiratorial wink, as he followed him and Kitty to the door.

"Have a good time, *son*," he said, and Jack winced at the amount of emphasis he'd placed on the word.

After walking Kitty to the rented carriage—which Jack's father had paid for—they were soon en route to Godalming for supper.

During the meal, Kitty did open up a bit. She asked practical questions about Jack's job and work. "Where do you stay when you're in port?" "How long do the crossings take?" et cetera. However, Jack could tell she was doing calculations in her head, thinking about all the time he'd be away from her.

The dinner of shepherd's pie ended on an amiable note, although Jack got the distinct impression that, when it came right down to it, the reserved Kitty had no more interest in marrying him than he did her.

He hoped that, given her reaction, this information would filter back to his old man. But unfortunately, it didn't. Clearly, Mr. Bex's mind was just as made up as his father's was because, in the days following the outing, all Jack heard from Col. Phillips—courtesy of Mr. Bex—was "how much Kitty had liked him." Jack wondered what sorts of conversations were actually taking place in the Bex household. He had to assume Kitty was receiving the same pressure he was.

"Why don't they all just butt out!" he thought crossly one night as he settled into bed. "A man *ought to* have a say in whom he marries, for Christ's sake!"

For the next several days, Jack and his father continued to argue about it, at times bitterly, right up until the time Jack boarded his train. And to make matters worse, Ethel made it clear whose side she was on.

The night before he left, while their parents were out visiting friends, the two had spent a quiet evening together in the living room. Jack, as usual, was in his armchair reading, while Ethel sat on the sofa knitting. The tension in the room was obvious. When Jack glanced up from his book, he noticed the furrows on Ethel's forehead were becoming so deep they appeared to be engraved.

Finally, perhaps inevitably, she broke the silence. "I know you feel put upon," she said slowly, her attention focused on the sweater sleeve she was making. "But have you noticed that our parents are getting old?"

Jack didn't answer. Frankly, the thought had never occurred to him.

Ethel looked over at him, and Jack could see a kind of desperation in her eyes.

"It's not unreasonable for them to want grandchildren, Jack."

"I never said it was," he said finally.

"But how would it help if you took a wife in Liverpool, or America, or some other far-off place?"

"Liverpool!" Jack scoffed to himself. "Not a chance in a million!"

However, when he didn't respond right away, Ethel cleared her throat and started to speak again. For some strange reason, Jack knew what she was going to say before she said it. And all he could think was, "Dear God, no. *Please don't.*"

"If dear Fred were still alive," Ethel said, "I'm certain this apartment would already be full of grandchildren."

There it was.

Fred.

Not once, in Ethel's entire life, had she uttered their dead brother's name in his presence. Until now.

"But he's not, Jack," she continued, her voice rising angrily. "He's *not!* So that responsibility falls to you!"

"That's right!" Jack thought. "Fred, the perfect one! Fred, the little angel who always did what mum and dad—and more importantly—big sister Ethel told him to!"

A part of him wanted to shout at Ethel, "I'm sorry! I'm sorry you feel bad about Fred! I'm sorry for his illness. And I'm sorry for how your own life has been affected by it. I truly am! I don't know why any of that happened! But I do know this: if Fred had lived, he *would not* have turned out as perfect as you think!"

He came very close to saying this, or at least part of it, but the moment passed, and he felt his anger dissipate.

Ethel resumed her knitting, as if nothing had happened. Once again, the clicking of her needles was the only sound in the room.

A few moments later, Jack stood up and grabbed his coat and gloves.

"Going for a walk," he said as he left the apartment.

"God, I need a smoke," he mumbled to himself.

— — —

Since Jack had only slept fitfully in his bunk the night before, he was a bit bleary-eyed the following morning when he went down to breakfast on C Deck. He quaffed several cups of tea just to keep his eyes open.

The dining room was quiet, save for the clink of "Book Man's" silverware on his plate. He and Jack were the only two in the room.

With amusement, Jack watched the enraptured expression on the gangly postal clerk's face as he cut his flapjacks into rectangular chunks and shoveled the pieces into his mouth, all without taking his eyes from his book.

Jack noticed the man's lips moved silently as he read.

"What in God's name is he reading?" Jack wondered, as he patted his stomach, drained his teacup, and got up from the chair. The postal clerk, as usual, didn't react.

"His feet could well be on fire," Jack thought, "and he probably wouldn't even notice."

Leaving the saloon, Jack made his way to the Boat Deck for a smoke. The weather was perfect. The sunshine and cool, salty air felt good on his face as he gazed out at the wide expanse of blue water surrounding the ship.

He knew he should relieve Harold—the boy's breakfast was getting cold—but he honestly didn't care. One of the benefits of being a first officer was you could set the schedule. And the second's job was to follow that schedule without complaint.

Besides, Jack reminded himself, hadn't he taken many a cold meal during his years as a second officer? Of course he had, and he was none the worse for it.

Jack had to give Harold credit, though. The boy, who had a good deal to say about a great many things, never complained about the cold meals, or the clanking elevators, even though Jack had arranged it so Bride took his rest from eight in the evening til two in the morning, when the infernal things were at their busiest. Jack had learned the ship's public areas closed at two—and, more importantly, the First Class Elevators were taken out of service at that time. Therefore, he decided two would be the time to take his own rest, when he could drift off to sleep undisturbed.

"The boy's okay," Jack thought again, as he pitched his butt into the sea.

As he made his way forward along the Boat Deck to the Marconi Room, Jack, despite all the tea, found himself still yawning. However, when he noticed a pretty young woman strolling toward him, he quickly covered his mouth.

The girl appeared to be sixteen or seventeen. She was obviously a First Class passenger, beautifully dressed, with blue eyes and perfectly coiffed blond hair. In one hand she held a parasol, and in the other, the hand of a much younger girl. This girl, Jack noticed, looked like a miniature version of the other one. Sisters, he assumed.

Jack was surprised—and slightly embarrassed—when he noticed that the older girl was *looking directly at him*. And not only that—she was *smiling!*

Jack tipped his cap to her—to both of them actually—and as they passed, the older girl spoke to him, which caused him to practically jump from his skin.

"Excuse me, sir," she said. "Are you an officer?" From her accent, it was clear she was American.

"First Marconi Officer," Jack told her, puffing his chest out proudly. He was delighted when the girl seemed impressed by his title.

"Then would you mind giving us a tour of the ship?" she asked, flashing a dazzling smile.

Jack was, naturally, deflated at this, since he had no choice but to admit he wasn't actually a *ship's* officer, but rather the ship's *wireless* officer.

Trying to hide his disappointment, Jack explained he was the person responsible for sending Marconigrams to land.

"Are those like telegrams?" the girl asked, her interest clearly piqued again.

"Yes," he said, "You see those wires?"

Jack pointed out the double sets of antennas running high above the ship.

"I see them, I see them!" the younger girl said excitedly, but Jack paid her little heed. His eyes were fixed on the steel-blue eyes of the beautiful older girl, as she squinted into the sky.

Once she located the aerial, Jack explained that electrical signals traveled along those wires, allowing messages to be sent through the air from ship to ship, and even from ship to land.

"The Marconi Room is in the back of the boat house, just behind the bridge." Jack said, pointing toward the bow. Then, trying his best to sound casual, he added: "I can give you a tour of that, if you like."

"I want to go! I want to go!" the younger girl said excitedly.

Jack was brought up short by this. With its expensive and fragile equipment, the Marconi Room was no place for children. He shuddered to think what would happen if something inadvertently got broken during their "illicit" tour.

As the younger girl smiled eagerly at Jack, he put on his most serious face.

"I'm sorry," he said. "It takes electricity to run the Marconigraph...which is very dangerous...especially for a little girl. But perhaps your big sister can come for a tour and tell you about it later?"

"Humph!!" the younger girl said, pouting.

Jack shot a smile at the older girl, whom he was pleased to see, appeared to be considering the offer.

"Could I send a telegram?" she asked, with a smile that could only be described as flirtatious.

"Marconigram," Jack corrected, his heart beginning to pound.

"Marconigram," she repeated, looking him directly in the eyes.

"Perhaps," Jack said, attempting to hold her gaze—and smile—as his heart began to thump, and his stomach turned to knots.

Back in the Marconi Room, Jack wondered whether the girl would take him up on his offer. Try as he might, he couldn't get her lovely face out of his mind.

As he sent out another Marconigram, instinctively translating the words from the slip of paper in his left hand into Morse dots and dashes with his right hand, a part of him was clearly elsewhere...what if she comes...and what if...he and the American girl ended up...?

But he couldn't complete the thought.

After Harold returned from breakfast, Jack had him take over the key so he could go to the washroom to freshen up. He wanted to look presentable, in the event of a visit. When he left the loo, he found his friend Jim Moody waiting in the hallway.

After exchanging pleasantries, Jack, trying to sound casual, said, "If you see a pretty American girl wandering around the hallway, would you make sure to escort her back here?

"A pretty American girl?" Jim grinned. *"Do tell...."*

Jack relayed to his friend the details of their brief encounter on deck earlier.

"Does she have a name, this pretty American girl?" Jim asked.

Jack was brought up short. He realized he never asked, and sheepishly told Moody so.

"Then I'll be on the look-out for Miss What's-her-name," Jim promised with a smirk, as he stepped into the washroom. *"Most definitely."*

Jack had been back at the key for a few hours, when Harold tapped him on the shoulder. Turning around, he saw Jim standing in the doorway with the American girl, who beamed happily at Jack. Gesturing for Harold to take the key, Jack got up awkwardly to greet her.

"Jack," said Jim in an oddly formal way, "I'd like to present *Miss Emily Ryerson.* And Emily, this is Mr. Jack Phillips."

Jack smiled at Emily, who smiled back. He felt his face flush.

Jim cleared his throat, and Jack, equally formally, said, *"Thank you, Mr. Moody."*

The two exchanged bemused glances, and Jack nodded at Jim, before turning his attention back to Emily. He was dimly aware that Jim lingered for a moment in the doorway before departing.

Jack, his face continuing to burn with embarrassment, showed Emily the Marconigraph, and demonstrated the use of the hydraulic tube.

Scribbling the word "Test" on a blank Marconi form, he sent it down to the Purser's Office. A few moments later, the brass cylinder returned with a whoosh. Jack opened it, and his face turned a deeper shade of crimson when he saw that some wiseacre below had defaced the message, making the word obscene by adding additional letters to the end. He quickly crumpled the paper.

"What did it say?" Emily asked

"Can't repeat it," Jack stammered. "Not exactly…fit for a lady."

Trying to recover from his embarrassment, Jack escorted Emily into the Silence Cabin, where he showed her the powerful transformers used to transmit the electronic waves to the ship's aerial antenna.

"Why is it called the 'Silence Cabin,'" she asked, "if it's so loud in here?"

"Well, see," Jack said, pointing out the room's extra thick walls and hatch-like doorway. "This room was constructed so the noise of the machinery stays inside."

For emphasis, he ushered her outside and after closing the door, pointed out the fact that the roar could barely be heard.

"See?"

"Yes," she said. "But I still don't know why it's called the 'Silence Cabin.'"

Jack didn't know how to respond to this, but luckily, his visitor moved on.

"What's in there?" Emily asked, pointing to the suite's other door.

"Oh," said Jack. "That's the bunk room. It's where he and I," he gestured over at Harold, "retire in the evenings."

"In the same bed?"

"No," Jack said. "We each have a bunk."

"A bunk?"

"You know, beds atop one another. Bunks."

Emily looked at him blankly. It was clear she had no idea what he was talking about. Jack knew what was coming next.

"Can I see?" she asked.

"Well…" Jack stammered, hoping that Harold was now occupied copying down a message. He didn't wish for him to overhear any of this. "Okay, why not!"

He opened the door quickly to allow her a peek inside.

"Wow," she said, with a look of utter fascination. "You sleep there?"

"Yes," Jack said, "On top," knowing that would be her next question. As he closed the door, his embarrassment returned full force. He tried changing the subject.

"How would you like to listen through the headphones? You can hear messages being transmitted."

Thankfully, Emily was fascinated by this idea.

Jack escorted her back to the desk, and tapped Harold on the shoulder. "Can she listen for a moment?"

"Sure," Bride said. "It's quiet now, anyway."

While Harold hovered nearby, Jack seated Emily in the chair, and carefully placed the earphones around the back of her head.

She listened for a moment, then smiled.

"Do you hear something?" Jack asked.

"I think so."

"Well, good," Jack said, lifting the headphones from her ears. He was once again struck by the beautiful, golden color of her hair.

She looked up at him and smiled.

"Didn't you say I could send a telegram?" she asked sweetly.

Harold snorted at this, and Jack found himself in an awkward position.

"You know, I could get in a great deal of trouble with the Purser's Office if they found out I sent a Marconigram that hadn't been paid for...."

"But you promised!" she said, tears beginning to well up in her blue eyes.

After giving Harold a "What can I do?" look, Jack finally relented.

"Okay. Okay."

He gave Emily a blank Marconi form and pen, and asked her to write down her message. "But keep it short, please," he said.

The room was silent as Jack and Harold watched Emily scratch out a few lines.

Dear Grammy, Writing to you from Titanic. Please don't tell father. Can't wait to see you. Emily

"Do you have her address?" Jack asked. "We'll need that."

Emily copied down her grandmother's address from memory. Jack noticed it was somewhere in Pennsylvania.

"Okay," he said conspiratorially, "Now you can watch me send it."

While Emily remained seated in the chair, Jack put the headphones back on and leaned over the desk. In a matter of moments, the message was sent.

"There," he said, "on its way."

Emily didn't respond. She merely flashed Jack another sweet smile.

"Now, Harold, if you don't mind taking the key?"

While Bride returned to his place at the Marconigraph, Jack offered Emily his arm. As she slipped her small hand through it, Jack could feel the electricity of her touch. He couldn't help but notice the sweet scent of her perfume.

Trying his best not to tremble, Jack escorted Emily down the hallway, and out through the door onto the Boat Deck.

"Mind the hatch," he told her, as they stepped over it.

"Would you like me to escort you to your room?"

"No, thanks," she said sweetly, "I can manage by myself." She pulled her arm from Jack's.

"Thank you, Mr. Phillips," she said.

"Please feel free to visit again. And you can bring your sister too, if you like."

"Oh, she's not my sister," Emily said with a laugh as she walked away. "She's just a girl I met on the ship."

Upon his return to the Marconi Room, Harold flashed Jack a sly smile.

"Owe you one," Jack said, as he returned to the seat Harold had just vacated.

From the boy's expression, Jack could tell he had every intention of collecting on it. However, at the moment, Jack couldn't have cared less. He was in his own world, thinking about the lovely Miss Emily Ryerson.

The rest of the day, and evening, passed quickly. Harold took his usual rest early, while Jack stayed alone at the key. Messages came and went at a rapid pace.

Shortly before two am, Harold awoke and relieved Jack. After having a smoke on deck, Jack went to the bunkroom to undress. In the darkness, his face got red once again as he remembered Emily's awkward visit there earlier.

His trousers had barely hit the floor, however, when he heard Harold cursing from the other room.

This was followed by footsteps, and a tentative knock at the door.

"What?"

"There's something wrong with the Marconigraph."

"What is it?" Jack asked irritably.

"I don't know," said Harold. "It's not working."

Jack quickly put his trousers back on and joined Harold at the set.

"The headphones are all right," Bride told him, "but for some reason, the key has lost power."

Harold demonstrated by pushing it down against the metal plate.

"See? No spark, nothing."

"Jesus H. Christ," Jack swore softly to himself.

This meant, while *Titanic* could still receive messages, she couldn't send any of her own.

Being at sea without a means of communication was not a good situation for a ship to be in. And the fact it was *Titanic*—the most advanced steamship in the world—was definitely ironic.

For Jack, it was a new experience. Never, in all his voyages, had a ship's wireless failed before. Even during that terrible hurricane back on the *Teutonic*, the Marconigraph had continued functioning properly.

"Well, let's find out what the hell's wrong with it," he grumbled.

Jack had the distinct impression, though, he wouldn't be getting much sleep.

"Bollocks," he cursed under his breath.

CHAPTER EIGHTEEN

YOU DON'T KNOW JACK

Paul, West Hollywood, California, January-February 2004

The bombshell of discovering the Marconi Room photo was of Harold Bride caused my project to come to a screeching halt. I put off writing anything more for almost a year. However, I continued to be drawn to the picture, which I kept in a file folder in my briefcase. Every time I came across it, I looked at it, and each time I did, I was struck by the uncanny resemblance.

"That's me. It is. *It's me.* I mean, it's Jack! The good Father Browne *had to have been mistaken.*"

I realized the photo could be digitally enhanced and compared with other photos of Bride.

"Someday I'd get around to doing it," I thought. Someday.

But business had begun to pick up, and I spent the next several months in a virtual whirlwind—hopping from one show to the next without a break. I finally got some time off during the Christmas holidays, and by the time my 41st birthday rolled around, I vowed—come hell or high water—to get back to the project.

My first order of business was to address the problem of the Father Browne photo. I organized my investigation around a simple proposition: that the priest had indeed misidentified the photo, and it was my job to look for evidence that could either support or refute this theory.

I started with some in-depth research on Father Browne. I learned that, just a few months after the disaster, he'd been invited to speak at a local college about his experiences aboard the ship. (Transcripts of his remarks were included in *Father Browne's Titanic Album*.)

During the lengthy speech, the priest took great pains to describe watching a brief performance by *Titanic*'s band (who, at that point, were renowned for heroically playing on deck while the ship was sinking); however, he made no mention of meeting either Phillips or Bride—or even, of visiting the wireless room—which seemed a curious omission, given the heroic (and equally famous) role the Marconi men had played during the tragedy. So it's possible that Browne's interactions with *Titanic*'s wireless officers had actually been minimal—or possibly, even, non-existent.

I also discovered that the priest hadn't actually created his *Titanic Album* until 1920. Eight years had passed between the time the photos were taken and when they were first captioned and put into that album. Thus, it would've been difficult for Father Browne to positively identify the subject of his photo—years after the fact—simply by looking at it, especially since the person was turned away, and it was a double-exposure.

However, my theory would only make sense if Browne hadn't known either Phillips or Bride before taking the photo, but rather, had learned their identities later from news reports of the disaster. In this hypothetical scenario, Father Browne would have merely slipped into the Marconi Room to take his picture, instead of being invited in by Jack.

I was pleased to discover—from reading *Father Browne's Titanic Album*—that this type of "run and gun" photography was not unheard of for Browne aboard *Titanic*. The priest had apparently also slipped into the private suite of a wealthy passenger (whom he didn't know) in order to get a picture of their opulent promenade. And just like with the Marconi Room photo, this snapshot had also been a double-exposure, which perhaps was a clue he'd been trespassing when he took *both* photos—and his haste had caused him to forget about advancing the film.

Of course, there was still the matter of the *other* photo in Browne's album, the one of Phillips that had been taken aboard the *Adriatic* several months before *Titanic* sank. The fact remained that if Browne had snapped this photo, he most likely would have known—or at least recognized—Jack, which would torpedo my misidentification theory.

Inspecting the picture closely, I noticed right away it appeared different from the rest of Father Browne's photographs. First off, the image appeared sharper—as if it had been taken with a camera with slightly better optics than the one Browne typically used.

Secondly, the style of this photo was markedly different as well. The two Marconi officers were positioned front and center in the frame—clearly the focus on the shot—with very little extraneous background detail. On the other hand,

Browne's *Titanic* photos had a completely different visual style. Frankly, they were better; the compositions were more artistic—oftentimes using interesting angles—and there was always a great deal of background detail in every frame.

The third thing I noticed about the *Adriatic* photo was that it appeared to have suffered damage at some point: a very large thumbprint could clearly be seen in the area of Jack's midsection. Flipping through the album, I couldn't find any other photos with this sort of imperfection—which suggested that the damage most likely hadn't occurred after the album was created. This begged the question: if the damage had occurred *prior* to the construction of the album, why hadn't the priest just gone ahead and printed a clean version of the photo? One answer might be that Browne didn't actually have this particular negative to print from, since he hadn't taken the picture.

As I continued studying the *Adriatic* photo, I realized there was even more damage than I'd previously seen. In a couple of places, the photo's edges appeared to have been torn. In fact, the picture didn't really look like a photograph at all. It seemed to have a raised border, as if it were a postcard that had been printed on a heavier stock of paper.

Then I noticed something else: in all four corners of the image were tiny round holes that looked suspiciously like thumbtack holes, as if the photo/postcard had been tacked to a corkboard for a period of time before being pasted into Browne's scrapbook.

Looking through the rest of Father Browne's album, the only other images I could find that appeared to have similar "thumbtack" holes were *Titanic* postcards that the author of

Father Browne's Titanic Album specifically stated were *not* taken by Francis Browne.

Thus, it was clearly possible that Father Browne had acquired the *Adriatic*/Jack Phillips photo, just like the *Titanic* postcards, some time after the sinking.

My theory was soon bolstered by the discovery that, at the time the *Adriatic* photo was presumably taken—in the fall of 1911—Father Browne was actually enrolled in a seminary in Dublin. Thus, it seemed unlikely he'd have been able to make the long train journey to Queenstown—which was the closest place he could've gotten access to the *Adriatic* during a voyage. And without a paid ticket, the priest couldn't have just "walked" onto the ship either. In order to meet Jack and take his picture on the Boat Deck, Browne would have had to "talk" his way aboard. This seemed like an excessive amount of hoops to jump through.

A few days later, I found something else that literally made me jump up and down. While looking through a book of reprinted newspaper accounts of the disaster, I came across a photo of Harold Bride that had been taken on April 20, 1912, just five days after the sinking. (It was published in the *New York Herald* the following day.)

Right away, I noticed something was wrong. Bride's hair was much too long. The man in Father Browne's Marconi Room photo seemed to have short hair—especially on top. He even had what appeared to be a slight bald spot. But Bride's hair in the *New York Herald* photo was long and unruly. It didn't seem possible for it to have grown that fast in just over a week.

This meant that the man in Father Browne's photo couldn't be Bride—and since *Titanic* didn't have a third Marconi officer—the only other person it *could have been* was Jack. At this point, I was 100 percent certain that Browne had miscaptioned the photo.

I was aware that this, by itself, proved nothing—at least as far as my past-life search was concerned. As Pat correctly pointed out when I told him, ultimately proving that Jack's picture had been misidentified for 84 years wouldn't prove I was his reincarnation; it would merely prove I'd been the first to notice the discrepancy.

True. But my amateur photo sleuthing had proven something to me: that my attachment to Jack Phillips wasn't based on delusion. As I saw it, there'd been too many bizarre and inexplicable incidents over the years for it *all* to be written off as coincidence.

I felt the time had finally come to proceed with my project.

I went back to writing my story. It seemed imperative to get it out of my head—and quickly!

CHAPTER NINETEEN

BETRAYAL

Jack, North Atlantic, April 13-14, 1912

Bundled up against the cold, Jack stepped out onto the Boat Deck for a cigarette. In the east, the sky was lightening, and he stood for several minutes watching the sun come up over the water.

"No matter how many times I see that," he thought, "it's always a thrill."

Physically, he felt pretty good, which was remarkable considering he and Harold had spent the remainder of the night trying to figure out what was wrong with the Marconigraph. Eventually they discovered the problem: some wire leads on the transformer had made contact with the metal housing that protected them and shorted out.

Jack ended up covering the bare wiring with electrical tape, and for now, the fix appeared to be working. This was a good thing, because otherwise, they'd have had no choice but to hook up the back-up Marconigraph, which had a range of less than fifty miles.

Since the main set could broadcast four hundred miles or more, Jack knew having to handle the volume of *Titanic* passenger messages with such a limited set would be a nightmare. Thus, he hoped the problem was solved for good.

Ditching his smoke, he returned to the Marconi Room, where Harold was still transmitting the messages that had come in while the Marconigraph had been down.

Yawning, he went to the bunkroom to try and salvage a couple of hours of shut eye.

However, once he was undressed and in bed, he found himself unable to sleep. He was physically exhausted, and yet, his mind refused to shut down. He thought of Emily, and the touch of electricity that had passed between them.

The big question was, would she return? He'd invited her…but that didn't mean she'd take him up on the offer.

Then he had an unsettling thought: what if the sole purpose of her visit had been to send that Marconigram? He scoffed at the notion. After all, hadn't she been writing to tell her grandmother she missed her? This was hardly earthshaking news. Besides, he didn't think Emily would've gone through the trouble of extricating herself from the company of her young friend, if she didn't have at least *some* interest in him.

"She'll come," he told himself forcefully, and he tried to imagine what the second visit would be like. Perhaps this time she'd allow him to escort her back to her room, which would give them time to talk privately, without Harold underfoot.

He hoped so, because he had so many questions. What had she been doing in Europe? With whom was she traveling? Where did she live?

As he drifted off to sleep, Jack thought once again of the scent of Emily's perfume, and the feel of her hand brushing past his arm.

However, all too soon, Harold was knocking loudly at the door.

"What time is it?" Jack said crossly. He felt like he'd barely closed his eyes.

"Eight," Harold replied. "I don't want to miss breakfast."

Jack got up, dressed, and returned to the Marconi Room to relieve Harold.

"I can bring you back something, if you like," the boy said, as he walked out the door.

"That would be great," Jack called after him, slipping on the headphones and trying to shake the weariness from his eyes.

Harold returned a half-hour later with a plate of eggs and bacon, courtesy, as he told Jack, of "Book Man."

"Yes, he was there," Harold replied, "and no, he never took his eyes from that blasted book."

"'Tis a wonder he doesn't stab his tongue with his fork," Jack said, as he began cutting his eggs.

"What do you suppose he's reading?" Harold asked.

"Probably a detective story…or murder mystery."

"The real mystery is why his wife hasn't killed him if he acts like that at home."

"How do you know he's married?"

"Well, he's got a ring, hasn't he?" Harold said indignantly.

"I hadn't noticed," Jack said with a laugh.

Once he finished eating, Jack asked Harold to spot him, so he could go to the washroom and clean up properly.

"Must make ourselves presentable for *Emily*," Harold teased.

"Perhaps," Jack responded, smiling slyly.

He returned a few minutes later, refreshed, and settled down to work. He was kept busy, both sending and receiving passenger messages, for the next several hours.

He took more than the usual number of smoke breaks as well, given that he was tired, and tobacco always perked him up. However, thoughts of Emily were never far from his mind, and he looked for her each time he went on deck, but unfortunately, he saw no sign of her.

"Maybe she's not coming," he thought darkly.

As the day wore on, and Emily still hadn't arrived, Jack's lingering disappointment turned to depression.

By evening, he was dog-tired, and he barely made it through his shift. He had Harold relieve him at midnight, and he stumbled from his clothes and collapsed in a heap on his bunk.

When he was awakened six hours later, he was foggy and disorientated. He dressed and went outside for a couple of smokes to help revive him. It sort of worked.

The morning was busier than usual. In addition to the passenger traffic, a series of navigational reports had started coming in. From what Jack could gather, the winter ice melt was drifting farther south than usual this year. The messages came from a variety of ships, and like all Master's Service Grams, had to be acknowledged and sent promptly to the bridge.

After Harold logged the messages, Jack wound up delivering a few of them himself, since it gave him the opportunity to grab a smoke afterward. On one such occasion, he saw Emily passing by the hatchway door.

He started to say something, but stopped when he realized she wasn't alone. She was walking arm-in-arm with Jim Moody, who was apparently in the midst of giving her a tour.

"Oh, great," Jack thought, noticing the younger girl was with them as well.

Waiting a few moments until the group had passed, Jack quietly stepped out onto the deck to watch them depart.

"And down here," Jack heard Jim say, "is the forecastle deck...."

He couldn't help but notice Emily was looking directly at Jim, and smiling as he spoke. And he also noted that Jim was likewise stealing sideways glances at her.

Jack felt his ears burn. "The bastard!" he fumed. "Some friend!"

At that moment, the younger girl turned and noticed Jack watching them.

She made a face at Jack, and stuck her tongue out for good measure, before turning her attention back to the "tour."

Jack stood there completely dumbfounded, until his feet were prodded into action when he saw the younger girl grab Emily's arm and say something to her.

Jack hurried back through the hatch to the Marconi Room.

"That was quick," Harold said, upon his return.

"I decided what I really wanted was a cup of tea," Jack said, taking the headphones from him. "Would you mind getting it? Two sugars."

Jack steamed about the situation the entire time Harold was off fetching his tea, and he continued to brood about it for several hours later. Even as he was kept busy with work, a part of his mind continued replaying the events. He seemed to remember Moody had been exceptionally flirtatious with Emily when he'd first escorted her into the Marconi Room.

"That opportunistic bastard," he said again under his breath.

At least part of his annoyance stemmed from the fact that, although Jack hated to admit it, he knew Jim was better looking than he was. During their previous voyages together on the *Oceanic*, Jack had discovered this perk of being Jim's friend. Ladies would lavish attention on them whenever they went to pubs, and Jack himself benefited by being in Jim's circle. This only made his betrayal tougher to take.

Jack's mood worsened when, later, while slipping out once again for a smoke, he found the weather, which had previously been sunny and warm, was now bitterly cold.

He tried braving it at first, however, since he didn't have his gloves or overcoat, he was soon shivering too hard. "Oh, bother," he said crossly, flicking his half-smoked butt into the sea.

Back in the Marconi Room, Jack tried focusing on the work at hand, but his mind kept returning, again and again, to Jim's betrayal. Even Harold knew something was wrong, but the boy had the good sense not to comment on it.

By the time the sun set later that day, Jack could see the skylight window above had fogged over. He assumed it was absolutely freezing outdoors, and this time, bundled himself up warmly before leaving the Marconi Room for dinner.

As he made his way down the passageway, Jack heard Moody's laugh coming from the bridge area ahead of him.

He grimaced, and quickly ducked through the hatchway onto the deck.

Dinner did nothing to improve Jack's spirits. After finishing his plate of pot roast and potatoes, Jack noticed he and "Book Man" were once again the only two left in the dining saloon.

Putting down his napkin, he began craving a smoke. However, the prospect of visiting the cold deck right now was not an enjoyable one.

"Don't suppose he'd mind if I lit up here," Jack thought, glancing over at "Book Man." "Heck, he probably wouldn't even notice."

But Jack had barely touched the match to the cigarette when Book Man looked up and glared sharply at him.

"Put that out at once!" he said angrily.

"What?" Jack said incredulously.

"Cigarettes are the devil's instruments!" Book Man said, his voice practically hissing.

Jack was indignant. He shoved off from the table and stormed over to him.

"You want me to put this out?" he said, glowering angrily at Book Man.

"Yes," the man said. "I do!"

"How about I put it out on that bloody book you're reading!"

The man slammed it shut and attempted to cover it with his hands.

"You wouldn't *dare!*"

"Oh, wouldn't I?" Jack said, his voice rising.

Then, looking down, he saw the small words printed in gold leaf on the book's cover: *Holy Bible.*

Instantaneously, he was overcome by a wave of nausea.

He returned to his seat, butted out the smoke on his dinner plate, and hurried from the room.

CHAPTER TWENTY

GOING UNDER AGAIN

Paul, West Hollywood & New York, NY, June-September 2004

By summer, I'd finally finished writing my story—and organizing the existing biographical material on Jack.

Then I moved on to step two: finding a past-life hypnotherapist. When I tried tracking down Janeen, I was unable to locate her, which was a bummer because I was hoping she could refer me to someone else.

I continued searching and eventually stumbled upon the website of a hypnotherapist in North Carolina[5] who claimed to have done hundreds of past-life regressions.

What was interesting about his site was it offered a guided regression you could listen to in the privacy of your own home.

---

[5] Identifying details have been changed due to privacy concerns.

The hour-long recording—which cost $20 bucks—promised to regress a person to *three* different past lives. I figured, what the hell, and ordered it.

After my credit card info went through, I was immediately able to download the MP3 to my laptop. Given my excitement, I had to try it out right away. By this time, Pat had gone to bed, so no one saw me lying on the couch as the taped regression began playing in my earphones.

The hypnotist used the same general techniques Janeen did: first the induction, followed by the regression. But he seemed to be coming from a different place with all of it.

I found myself rolling my eyes—even though they were closed—when he asked me to imagine myself "nestled inside a cocoon of white light," which he claimed was necessary to ensure the regression only revealed things that would be for my "Highest Good."

I had no idea what he was talking about—it was all too New Agey for me.

Despite my misgivings, however, I began to slip into hypnotic trance. My arms and legs became heavy, and soon I was unable to move.

About twenty minutes into the recording, the hypnotist switched gears to prepare me for the "journey" to the past lives.

"Imagine," said his voice in my ear, "that there's a beautiful, grassy hill in front of you. You start walking up the hill, and you notice the grass is covered with thousands of purple flowers. Pause for a moment to take in the flowers…then continue on your way up the hill. You notice there's something bright at the top of the hill—something that reflects the sunlight—but you can't quite make out what it is. So you keep walking, and as you get closer, you realize it's a mode of transportation. It might be a small plane, or a mini-bus, or even an automobile...but take a moment now and just see it in your imagination, because this vehicle will be taking you back to your past lives."

This was a very different technique from the one Janeen had used back in 1996, and I had to admit, it was kind of cool.

I found myself picturing a DeLorean. "Might as well go with the whole *Back to the Future* thing," I thought.

After the hypnotherapist instructed me to imagine reaching the top of the hill, he asked me to step inside my transport vehicle, which I did, feeling very Marty McFly-ish. Then the hypnotist informed me that my vehicle was starting to move and, as it picked up speed, it would turn back the pages "on the calendar of my life."

"The life you visit," the hypnotist said, "has been chosen by your 'Higher Consciousness' to help you better understand your current life circumstances."

Then the hypnotist told me the vehicle had stopped and I was free to exit. I realized I shouldn't have imagined myself getting into a DeLorean—they're a pain to get out of.

"Where do you find yourself right now?" he asked. "What's the first thing you see? What are you feeling?"

I wasn't seeing or feeling anything particularly, except the growing suspicion this was a waste of time. However, since I was still under hypnosis, I had no choice but to wait to be "awoken" at the end of the tape.

Then I had a panicked thought. "What if he never wakes me?"

"Now I want you to travel to where you live in this lifetime. How would you describe your home?" the hypnotist continued, unaware of my distress.

"Now go inside and see the people you live with. Who are they?"

At this moment, I began to see flashes of images, but they faded quickly before I could latch onto any one in particular. It was kind of like the spooky videotape from the movie *The Ring*: a series of random images that didn't make a lot of sense.

"I want you to locate a mirror in your home and look deeply into it. (pause) How would you describe your appearance?"

Naturally, I saw images of Jack in his Marconi uniform.

"This isn't right," I thought. "I'm seeing Jack because I'm hoping to. My mind is just making this up."

At this point, I really wanted to turn off the MP3. However, since I was still in a hypnotic stupor, I couldn't simply open my eyes and get up. I knew I'd have to suffer through it.

The hypnotist continued asking questions, leaving periods of silence for me to think about the answers.

"How you spend most of your time in this life? Do you work—or are you employed—outside the home?"

Silence.

"What part of the world would you say this is? What's the ground cover like? The scenery?"

More silence.

As I lay listening to the guy's voice, I kept hoping it would be over soon.

Finally, I got my wish.

"At the count of five, I want you to move forward in time to the death you experienced in this lifetime."

Despite myself, I began seeing fragments of images, all involving the sinking of the *Titanic*. However, I believed none of it. I was sure my imagination had kicked into high gear and was giving me what I'd asked for.

"And now, I want you to transition *past* the death..." the disembodied voice intoned.

"Thank God!" I thought.

"...and into the spirit realm. What do you see? What do you feel?"

I'm fairly certain the only thing I was feeling was gratitude.

"Now it's time to return to your mode of transportation," the hypnotist said at last, "which will once again take you back, through the years, so you can experience another lifetime...."

"Oh, no," I thought. I'd forgotten the recording had promised to show me glimpses of *three* past lives.

At this point, I really checked out, trying not to listen to anything the hypnotist was saying. Thus, I was able to ignore the interminable visits to the second and third "lives." However, my ears definitely began to perk up when the hypnotist finally announced that it was time to return to my time-hopping vehicle.

Needless to say, I was all too happy to slip back into the DeLorean.

A few minutes later, right before the hypnotist began his countdown to wake me up, he added one final directive. "Each time you play this MP3, my voice will take you deeper and deeper into trance, and this regression will become even more effective for you."

"I should hope so," I thought, as the hypnotist began slowly counting to five to bring me back to consciousness. I awoke and stretched, powered down my laptop and headed off to bed.

Remembering what the hypnotist had said—that each time I listened to the MP3 I'd find it more effective—I decided to give it another try a few nights later. By this time, I had little hope for success. However, given that I was still working and didn't have time to hunt down a "real" hypnotherapist, I figured I had nothing to lose.

Unfortunately, though, I was too tired, and fell asleep sometime during the induction. I awoke in the middle of the night, long after the recording had finished. But at least one question was answered. I'd awakened from the trance on my own, without having to be told to do so. Thus, I could put aside my fear of not being able to wake in the event of a computer crash or power outage.

About a week later, I tried the MP3 again. Before I slipped on the earphones, I'd decided this would be it. As far as I was concerned, there were only two possible outcomes: either third time's the charm, or three strikes you're out.

I figured I should try and take it more seriously—"cocoons of white light" and all. This meant losing the DeLorean and replacing it—in my mind's eye—with a more sensible vehicle. (I ended up settling on a gleaming white monorail.)

"No wisecracking," I admonished myself, as the recording started, and I settled back on the couch.

Soon, I was imagining stepping through the monorail's now-open doors. But still, I saw and felt nothing.

The hypnotist announced that he'd be asking me a series of questions to help me "better experience" this past life.

"The questions may be answered by 'visions,' or sounds, or 'feelings,'" he said, "but it's important for you to allow the information to flow without judgment."

The hypnotist explained that letting the conscious mind "pick apart" the things I was experiencing would only serve to shut down the channel of information, so he encouraged me to stay in the moment as much as possible.

"I'll try," I thought.

"Now I want you to travel to where you live in this lifetime. How would you describe your home?"

Suddenly, I saw the fuzzy image of a house. An older house, something that looked like a grandparent's home.

Then a series of images began flashing before my eyes. I got a whirlwind tour of what appeared to be a different dwelling: an upstairs bedroom with a window to the street below; a rear kitchen; a living room that opened to the right, and a round wall mirror hanging below a cherry-wood staircase to the upper floors.

I saw "Jack" primping in front of the mirror. He was wearing a crisp white shirt and dark tie beneath his Marconi jacket, the familiar cap perched on his head. This time, I didn't scoff at the image. I let it play out without evaluation.

"Who are the people that are most important to you in this life?" the hypnotist asked.

I heard a woman's voice (presumably his mother) calling from a different part of the home. "Jack!"

The hypnotist announced he'd give me time to interact with my "loved ones." He instructed me to identify the positive and negative aspects of each relationship.

In the silence that followed, I saw images of "Jack's" mother as she doted on him. I could see her smiling face, and the look of affection in her eyes. Then I saw the father. The man sat rigidly on an armchair in the old-fashioned living room, reading his newspaper.

Right away, I "knew" Jack was estranged from his dad. I saw brief fragments of arguments, and I got the idea that Jack—who was a bit spoiled—was often mouthy toward his father, especially when he was younger. And the dynamic only became more dysfunctional when Jack grew older.

"What's your name?" the hypnotist said. "What do people call you?"

Jack, of course, Jack Phillips.

"How do you spend most of your time in this life? Do you work—or are you employed—outside the home?"

Now the scene shifted, and I saw myself transmitting messages on a wireless set.

"At the count of five, I want you to move forward in time to the death you experienced in this lifetime...."

Once again, I saw various scenes from the sinking: the tilting deck; the pandemonium right before the end; and Jack, alone, clinging to the railing as the ship plunged into the sea.

Even hypnotized, my head began to reel. It wasn't just the obvious stuff—I was seeing new things about Jack's life (the layout of his childhood home and the interactions with his family members) that I hadn't read or considered before. I just wanted to wake up and write everything down. I didn't want to forget a thing.

But the journey wasn't over. There were still *those other lives* to contend with.

I reluctantly returned to the monorail, which the hypnotist told me would soon be transporting me back to another lifetime.

"Your 'Higher Consciousness' has picked this life to add insight into your current situation," he said, "and also to help you better understand the life you've just seen."

Given that the life was supposed to relate to the first, I decided to pay attention and go with it. And I'm glad I did, because this second "life" came right out of left field.

Or should I say bog?

I saw myself as an Irish peat farmer—a big oaf of a guy with a huge neck and massive shoulders and arms—but who also had a large, prominent cleft lip that was painful to look at.

The man lived in a stone and wood house with a rock wall in front. It was his parents' home, and he lived there, long after their deaths, for the remainder of his life.

Inside the house—which was what I would call a cottage—there was an ornate Victorian mirror, which the man rarely glanced at. Secretly, he wanted to get rid of it, but didn't dare; it had been his mother's, and he knew she wouldn't have wished him to change anything about their home.

The man worked hard each day cutting the heavy peat from the bog adjoining his house. He rarely left the property. I got the sense that wagons would pull up and collect the peat after he'd prepared it and tied it into bundles.

When he occasionally ventured out—on walking trips to the local store—the neighborhood children constantly teased him. I could hear their high voices as they shouted insults from their hiding places. None of the kids would dare say such things to his face, of course, since they knew if he caught them, he could easily have wrung their necks.

The man had few friends—outside of business acquaintances—and was never married.

At some point, the hypnotist asked, "What's your name? What do people call you?"

The answer came swiftly. *John. John McGilvery.*

Then the hypnotist asked if I had any insight about how the life I was "seeing" related to the previous one—or to the life I was currently living.

I couldn't immediately see the connection to my own life, but I instantly understood the connection to Jack's: after a life as a scared recluse, Jack would have wanted to get out and see the world. This certainly explained his wanderlust.

And of one thing I had little doubt: although he wasn't aware of it, the handsome Jack was delighted, each time he looked in the mirror, that he *didn't see John McGilvery's face staring back at him.*

This could explain his cockiness.

I was so blown away by this "second life" that I found myself unable to stop processing the things I'd seen. Thus, I ended up drawing a blank when faced with the recording's "third"—and final—life. However, as soon as the hypnotist awakened me, I jumped up excitedly from the couch.

Closing out the MP3 program, I opened up a Microsoft Word file and began writing down the things I'd experienced. It was the rudimentary beginning of a journal I'd keep for the remainder of the project.

And as I continued digesting the information, I came to the same conclusion I'd previously reached after my first regression: the unexpected appearance of the peat farmer—like the hapless native before him—served to convince me that the stuff with Jack had also been real.

A couple nights later, I did a web search for Ireland and "peat farmers." At some point in my life, I'd certainly heard the words "peat bogs," but I hadn't realized peat was farmed as such. I soon discovered that it was. The peat (a form of heavy moss) was extracted, dried out and used for fuel in fire-places, since wood was at a premium in 19th century Ireland.

Despite the fact that I couldn't be certain of the spelling, I also did a quick genealogical web search for "John McGil-very." I learned the McGilvery/McGillivray name was Scottish—not Irish—but, in a British census form from 1881, I did come across a John McGilvery who'd been born in County Cork, Ireland in 1863.

At the time the census was taken, however, this John McGilvery had been 18 years of age and enlisted in the Brit-ish Army. Since the census preceded Jack's birth by only six years, I knew it couldn't be my "John"—who was clearly much older when he died.

But it meant that there *had been* McGilverys living in Ire-land during the 19th Century.

Over the next several weeks, as I continued mulling over the regression—and "John McGilvery's" sad story—I came to realize that there were some pretty obvious parallels between his life and mine.

For instance, my predilection for extreme "nesting" when-ever I was home alone and not working—whether it be on weekends or during brief periods of unemployment. In those instances, it often required a great deal of internal prodding to get myself to leave the house—for any reason, and even the flimsiest excuse not to...or delay the trip...would invariably be jumped on. Once I was out and about, however, I always enjoyed myself—which led to thoughts like, "This is so much fun!" and "Why don't I do this more often?" And yet, as soon as I returned home, the default "hermit switch" would reset once again.

Another parallel I had to acknowledge was my deep-seated belief in my physical unattractiveness. The funny thing was, I could look in a mirror, or at a photo of myself, and objectively say, "Hey, you're not a bad-looking guy...." And yet, there was *always* another part of me, a deeper one, that just didn't believe it...which created a great deal of self-consciousness in social situations.

I realized that both of these traits could be the direct result of psychological conditioning in this life...given that I'd spent so many formative years as "the fat kid"; however, having suppressed memories of a past life as an Irish "Boo Radley" could have a similar effect...and either way, the connections were interesting to think about.

My current project—producing segments for a reality show for the TBS network—took me to New York City in early September. One afternoon, I found myself taking a cab from our location in Central Park to the midtown hotel where the crew was staying.

Since it was the first day of school in New York, there was lots of traffic on Fifth Avenue as parents began picking up their kids. While the cab navigated the clogged streets, the driver, who was Indian, started talking about his own children.

I must admit I barely paid attention; I was thinking about the work calls I had to make when I got back to the hotel.

But then, out of nowhere, the cabbie began telling me a story about his two-and-a-half-year-old son. Apparently, the boy was afraid of balloons. He was scared of the sound they made when they popped.

One day, according to the cabbie, the kid told him he was afraid of the "balloon-popping" sound because it reminded him of the time when he was working in a restaurant and a black man came in and shot him.

I was confused at first—not sure what the taxi driver was implying. But as his words sank in, I asked if he was referring to reincarnation.

"Yes," he said, matter-of-factly. "My son remembers *before.*"

We exchanged glances in the rear-view mirror. I smiled and nodded.

The cab driver, sensing he was in like-minded company said, "A lot of people here don't understand about that."

"That's true," I said, "but I believe it...because I also remember *before.*"

I was smiling when I left the cab. "It's interesting," I thought, "how one connection can make your day."

The conversation with the cabbie hadn't exactly been a sign from heaven; however, it nevertheless served as a gentle reminder that my project was gathering dust at home, and I needed to get back to it.

It was finally time to step up to the plate. I needed to find a flesh-and-blood hypnotherapist.

CHAPTER TWENTY-ONE

"SILENCE! SILENCE! SILENCE!"

Jack, North Atlantic, April 14, 1912

After his argument with "Book Man," Jack hurried back to the Marconi Room and relieved Harold, who went off to find his own supper. Before he left, Bride popped his head back into the room.

"'Nother ice notice came in," he told Jack, "and I took it to the bridge."

"Very good," Jack said, and returned to the set, where he was happy to discover the ship was now in wireless range of the land station at Cape Race, Newfoundland. And although the signal was still faint, Jack knew it would strengthen as they continued westward.

This was good news, because it meant that, for the remainder of the crossing, he would be able to relay passenger messages directly to land stations, rather than having to utilize the services of Marconi officers on other ships.

After exchanging pleasantries with the Cape Race operator, Jack started taking down the Marconigrams the land station had been saving for him. There were several, and he was kept busy for over an hour. He was barely aware that Harold had returned and shuffled off to the bunkroom to rest.

Previously, the boy had agreed to once again relieve him at midnight, to allow him the opportunity to finally get caught up on sleep.

At one point, after Jack had copied down yet another Marconigram, his Cape Race communication was suddenly interrupted by another steamer who, capitalizing on a moment of dead air, began sending Jack a message. It read: *"From MMU to MGY and all east bound ships. Ice Report,"* followed by some latitudinal and longitudinal coordinates, and then, *"Saw much heavy pack ice and great number large icebergs, also field ice, weather good, clear."*

Since Jack didn't have maps, tools or navigational skills, he had no way of knowing that the report outlined a treacherous, miles-wide plot of ocean that *Titanic*, at that very moment, was steaming through at high speed.

After confirming receipt of the message, however, Jack wasn't sure how to handle it. If it were an official notice meant for *Titanic*'s captain, it would be marked MSG, which meant he would be required to take it to the bridge at once. But this message didn't say MSG, so it obviously wasn't a normal Captain-to-Captain message.

Jack scrutinized the sending ship's call sign, which he didn't recognize. Looking it up, he learned that it was the

Mesaba, a cargo vessel registered to the Atlantic Transport Line.

Given the message contained navigational information, Jack knew it should be taken to the bridge. However, since Harold was off duty, it meant Jack would have to bring it there himself.

He looked at the ship's clock. It was just after 9:30 pm. Jack knew Moody worked the bridge during the 8 pm-12 am shift, so a visit would certainly mean bumping into him. Jack grimaced as he recalled the sound of his former friend's raucous laughter from earlier.

Pursing his lips, Jack decided that, no, he didn't really wish to see Jim right now. Especially when there were still other passenger messages to attend to.

"It can wait 'til midnight," he thought, "when Harold takes over."

Meanwhile, he continued taking down incoming messages, and when they were done, he began transmitting his own back to Cape Race. At one point, he noticed the Marconigram he was sending was from a *Titanic* passenger named *A. Ryerson*.

Jack paused for a moment, mid-transmission, to read the whole thing.

"Thanks for the condolences. Children are fine. Concerned about Emily. Refuses to leave room, even for dinner. Will see you in Syracuse. A."

Jack was bewildered. As he turned over the contents of the message in his mind, his eardrums nearly exploded.

Another ship had begun transmitting, and its signal was extremely loud. Jack adjusted his headphones with one hand, as he began scrawling down the message with the other. He became irritated when he realized the communication was not addressed to any ship, or to any one, in particular. It was merely operator "chatter."

This was one of his pet peeves. Since there was only one main communication frequency that everyone had to use, Jack hated it when bored Marconi officers tied it up making small talk with other operators—especially when there were other people around with *real* work to do.

"Selfish bastard," he thought.

Silence! Silence! Silence! he fired back at the offending ship. *You're jamming me. I'm busy working Cape Race.*

After apologizing for the interruption, Jack resumed sending the Ryerson message. Once it was done, he stamped the form, added the time of delivery, and put it on the stack of sent messages.

As he worked to clear the backlog, a part of Jack's mind wondered about the mystery presented by the Ryerson message.

"Condolences?" For what?

"Concerned about Emily. Refuses to leave room?" Say again?

Jack recalled Emily's lovely face. Hadn't she been out and about on deck several times during the past few days?

Jack had no way of knowing, but *A. Ryerson* was actually Emily's father, Arthur. And the person he was speaking about wasn't Emily, but her mother, who went by the same name.

As Jack puzzled over the mystery, he had an unsettling thought. Perhaps if he thumbed back through the logbook, he might find additional messages sent to *A. Ryerson* that could help shed light on the mystery.

Jack realized this was the ultimate no-no. He had absolutely no business getting involved in Emily's private affairs.

Besides, he reminded himself, hadn't the girl made it perfectly clear she had no interest in him? So why, then, should he still care about her?

But even so, he continued to think about her pretty face, and mull over the contents of *A. Ryerson*'s message.

Once he was done sending to Cape Race, he signed off. Then he updated the logbook, and began organizing the stacks of incoming messages.

As he stood momentarily to stretch his legs, he felt the ship shudder slightly. However, by the time he was consciously aware of it, the sensation had stopped. After looking around for a moment, he went back to what he was doing.

Soon the messages were typed and loaded into the brass cylinder for the Purser's Office. Then, shortly after they were sent, Jack felt the ship's engine's shutting down.

"That's odd," he thought.

At that moment, Harold, stifling a huge yawn, stepped into the Marconi Room.

"What's going on?" he asked.

"Dunno," Jack said. "Maybe we threw a propeller."

"Threw a propeller? *Titanic*?"

"Sure," said Jack nonchalantly. Previously, he'd noticed Harold was particularly gullible upon waking up.

"We might even have to go back to Belfast for repairs," he told the boy solemnly.

"You think so?" Bride exclaimed.

"I don't know," said Jack, suddenly weary of the joke. "What I do know is I'm going to bed. I feel like I could sleep for a week!"

As he cleaned up the desk for Harold, Jack noticed the partially written Marconigram form containing the chatter message that had interrupted his work earlier. He balled it up, and dropped it into the waste paper bin beneath the desk.

"I cleared the backlog," he told Harold, stifling a yawn. Gesturing to the ship's clock above, he said, "Remember you've got the news service at midnight...."

Harold nodded. As both he and Jack knew, the Marconi land station in Cape Cod began broadcasting the day's news report—on a special frequency—promptly at 10:30 pm (local time) each evening, and it was their job to transcribe the items for the ship's newspaper, which the Purser's office typed up overnight.

As Harold took a seat in front of the Marconigraph, Jack considered going out for a smoke, but given the cold, decided against it. He knew his body needed sleep more than tobacco.

Returning to the bunkroom, he began to undress.

"*That* was a poor day," he mumbled to himself, as he unfastened his trousers.

Suddenly, there was a strange voice just outside the door.

Rubbing his eyes, it took him a moment to place it: Captain Smith, the commander of *Titanic*.

"What's he doing here at this hour?" he wondered, straining to overhear the conversation.

"I need you to be ready," Captain Smith was saying, "in case we have to send out a distress call."

"Sir," Jack heard Harold repeat, *"distress call?"*

Bride's question hung in the air. Jack's eyes widened.

"Yes," Captain Smith said brusquely. "Where's the first officer?"

"Right here, sir," Jack called, stumbling back into his trousers. He returned to the Marconi Room, still tucking in his shirt.

"We've struck an iceberg," Captain Smith told him, "and the carpenters are surveying the damage below decks. We may need you to issue a distress call. I'll let you know. But do not..." he paused a moment for emphasis, "...speak of this, *with anyone,* until I return."

"Yes, sir," Jack said.

Brushing past Harold, Jack took his place in front of the Marconigraph. He put the headphones around his neck, rather than over his ears, so he'd be ready when the captain returned.

Harold plopped down into the chair beside him, and, despite the captain's directive, started up right away.

"An iceberg! We actually hit a 'berg?"

Jack didn't respond, hoping instead Harold would take a clue from his silence and shut up. But he didn't.

"All those ice reports we sent to the bridge," he said, shaking his head, "and she goes and hits one, anyway!"

Jack, however, wasn't thinking of the messages he or Harold had run to the bridge earlier that day. He was thinking of the one marked "Ice Report" that had come in a couple hours earlier, but which he had, in fact, completely forgotten about.

"Where was it?" he wondered.

Looking down at the desk, he could see the edge of it, buried beneath the stack of blank Marconigram forms.

He considered reaching for it, but decided against it. Not with Harold hovering so close.

"You don't think the ship will sink, do you?" the boy asked.

"How should I know!" Jack snapped angrily, finally turning around to give Harold a stern look. However, seeing the boy's hurt expression, he softened and said, "Look, the captain asked us to be quiet about this. I suggest we follow his instruction."

Harold nodded, and looked down at his hands. But, for Jack, the silence was no better, as the boy was literally breathing over his shoulder.

"Why don't you go and keep watch for the captain," he told him at last.

To his relief, Harold went to the doorway at once.

After he was certain Bride's attention was elsewhere, Jack shuffled through the papers on his desk. Pulling out the undelivered message from *Mesaba* marked "Ice Report"—he reread it in its entirety, bit his lip, and returned the form to the bottom of the stack.

Guilty thoughts began rising in his throat, and he tried pushing them away. He knew he needed to think clearly now.

"Could the ship actually sink?" he wondered. It hardly seemed possible, and yet, the fact that the engines were shut down and *Titanic* was adrift at sea had to count for something.

Jack searched his memory. He could not find one other instance where a steamer he'd worked on had stopped in the middle of the ocean.

"At least we aren't in physical danger," he thought, "even if, God forbid, the ship eventually sank." He knew there were other steamers around; for instance, that fool who'd interrupted him while he'd been working Cape Race. His transmission had been so loud it had practically busted open his eardrums. This, Jack knew, meant that his ship was close.

He froze. *What had that fool been going on about?*

Then he remembered, with growing horror, that the chatter message, too, had contained something about ice.

He glanced over at Bride, who was now leaning against the doorjamb, arms crossed over his chest. Seeing Harold was occupied, nervously looking both ways down the hallway, Jack seized his chance. He reached into the trash bin to retrieve the crumpled message.

His eyes bugged out as he read and, for the first time, *comprehended* the entire thing.

"Say, old man, we are stopped and surrounded by ice...."

"Dear God in heaven," Jack thought, the full effect of the words hitting him.

He realized, with self recrimination, that he should have taken the time to inquire whom the chatterer was, and to discern why he'd been going on about ice. Surely, it would only have taken a moment to respond to the man and ask him what his business was, instead of telling him to shut up and get lost.

What if the ship does sink?

His mind boggled at the thought. This wasn't just any ship...it was *Titanic*...the largest and most expensive steamer ever built! If it were to founder, the loss would be incomprehensible. And people would surely find out that he'd foolishly not delivered messages involving ice to the bridge...and they might...they might...he couldn't even let himself complete the thought. He knew it would mean the end of his career.

"How could I have been so stupid?!?" he thought.

Just a few moments later, as Jack wrestled with his dark thoughts, the captain returned. Jack stopped breathing until he heard what Smith had to say.

"I need you to issue a distress call."

Captain Smith handed Jack a slip of paper with navigational details written in large block letters.

"This is our location. Make sure you transmit this *exactly.*"

The captain's eyes locked on Jack's. He was struck by the intensity of the old man's expression.

"Do you understand?" he said, "We can't afford an error."

Jack nodded. But once again, bile began rising in his throat. Calm down, calm down, he told himself. "What call should I use, sir?" he asked.

"The international call for distress. That's it."

Captain Smith turned to go, but Jack called him back.

"Sir, if a ship responds, what should I tell them?"

"That we're sinking by the head, and require assistance, at all possible speed."

"Right away, sir."

Jack turned back to the Marconigraph, and as he began tapping out the message, started shivering uncontrollably. His very insides felt like they'd turned to ice.

"Dear God, what have I done?"

A fresh wave of bile rose in his throat, nearly choking him.

CHAPTER TWENTY-TWO

THE HYPNOTHERAPIST

Paul, West Hollywood, California, October-November 2004

Despite my previous fears, it only took a simple web search to locate a Los Angeles-based, past-life hypnotherapist. In fact, as luck would have it, the guy had a home office just a few blocks away from my apartment. On the morning of the appointment, I dug out my trusty tape recorder, installed a fresh tape, and headed out.

As I walked down Santa Monica Boulevard, I was nervous—but excited as well. This had been far too long in coming!

Mark Benton[6] met me at his apartment door. He was a good-looking guy in his early thirties, with a perfect smile and an even more perfect Berber carpet. He asked me to take off

---

[6] Name changed out of privacy concerns.

my shoes. I didn't complain, although I was grateful to discover the socks I was wearing weren't hole-y.

The hypnotherapist's living room was set up like an office, with comfortable furnishings hidden from the entryway by a tasteful Asian screen.

I pulled the tape recorder from my pocket. "You don't mind if I record the session, I hope."

His perfect smile faded. "Actually," he said, "I don't allow recordings."

I looked at him quizzically.

"Hypnotic past-life therapy is similar to traditional therapy," he said, "and just as a psychiatrist wouldn't allow a patient to record a session, neither can I."

Noticing I was taken aback by this, he went on to explain, "Given the nature of the therapy, excerpts from a recording, if used out of context, could prove problematic for everybody."

"For instance," he added, "if you start talking about killing somebody in a past life...."

Trying to mask the disappointment I felt, I nodded and put the recorder back into my pocket.

I didn't say anything to him, but his comment had struck a nerve.

Killing someone in a past life? How about *1,500 someones?*

. . .

Years earlier, after my eventful visit to England, while I was still reeling from the eerie feeling of déjà vu I'd experienced in Jack's hometown, I decided to try and learn a little bit more about him and his life.

I realized that, despite the many books I'd read on *Titanic*, my only other experience with Walter Lord's *A Night to Remember* was having it read to me in the second grade. So I went and picked up a copy at a vintage bookstore, and thumbing through the index, looked up everything Lord had written about Jack.

To say I was stunned by the discovery that he'd blown off some pivotal ice warnings in the hours leading up to the disaster would be an understatement. The word *devastated* came closer to the truth.

Closing the book, I was overcome by a profound feeling of shame.

Previously, the idea of having past-life memories...the idea of trying to find out if I'd lived before...had been kind of fun. However, at that moment, everything changed. It felt like I'd ripped open a scab...and tapped into an endless well of sorrow and regret. I found myself behaving in a way that was totally unlike me.

In fact, I completely broke down. Thankfully, my partner, Pat, was not there to see the pitiful sight: me, collapsed in a heap on the living room floor, sobbing my eyes out.

I decided not to tell him about it right away. Up to that point, I'd shared even the tiniest detail involving my *Titanic* project. But this was different. Frankly, it felt like a guilty secret.

I spent several days trying to sort through my feelings. I kept asking myself, "Where is this coming from? Why do I feel such an incredible amount of guilt over this?"

But when I stopped to think about it, I realized that guilt had *always* ruled my life.

At work, I took responsibility for things that went wrong—even for things that weren't my fault. I just rolled up my sleeves and dived right in to try and solve the problem. And sure, professional managers were *supposed to be* accountable for the productivity of their departments—including, at times, taking the blame for mistakes made by their employees. However, with me it went deeper. My initial reaction, upon hearing *any kind of bad news*, was an unshakable feeling of guilt; I somehow *believed* it had been my fault—and it was up to me to make it right.

One time, a woman I worked with looked incredulously at me, while I was lamenting about something well beyond my control, and smirked, "C'mon, get off the cross. We need the wood."

I laughed heartily at this, grateful she'd relieved the tension, and yet her comment nevertheless underscored a valid point. Feelings of guilt went beyond the norm for me. They were deeply embedded in my psychological makeup.

One reason for this could be my Catholic upbringing. There's an old joke about how Jews invented guilt, but Catholics perfected it. From my experience, that was true enough. And although I had, in the course of my life, come to reject Catholic teachings on spiritual matters, I realized that I'd done so intellectually. But had I, despite my rational efforts, been able to eradicate them *emotionally?*

It was another example of the chicken and the egg. Was I reacting so strongly to Jack's sad story because of my own psyche, which was shaped in *this lifetime* by a variety of factors—including a Catholic upbringing? Or had my guilt-riddled psyche actually been created *in a previous lifetime* by Jack's regrettable actions?

The question remained.

After several days of processing this new information about Jack and *Titanic*, I finally decided to share what I'd learned with Pat. Just as I feared, the results weren't pretty. I broke down completely as I attempted to relay to him the events in *Titanic*'s wireless room on the night of the sinking. It took me several minutes to get through it. I found myself starting and stopping many times.

And compared to the silent tears that had flowed while we'd watched the film version of *A Night to Remember*, these tears were full-fledged histrionics that were scary in their intensity. As I sobbed my eyes out in front of him, I could see the growing concern on Pat's face. I couldn't tell, though, if he was merely sad for me, or if he feared I was losing it.

And it didn't just happen with Pat. For the next two years, every person to whom I opened up about my supposed past-life connection to Jack was treated to the exact same show.

And again, this was nothing like my standard MO. I was generally even-tempered—not prone to emotional outbursts. Sure, I'd occasionally lose my temper. Yes, I was often sarcastic. However, the one thing I wasn't was a blubbering idiot.

Except, apparently, when talking about events that had occurred five decades before I was born.

— — —

As I stood in Mark Benton's living room, dealing with my disappointment about his "no taping" rule, he led me to a couch to begin the session.

As it turned out, it didn't matter that my tape recorder had been banished. Mark didn't plan to regress me during our first meeting, anyway. It was basically a "get to know you" session.

He explained his treatment focused on allowing patients to "re-experience" past-life traumas, in order to overcome their lingering effects.

"So he does pretty much what Janeen does," I thought.

But, as he continued, I realized his approach was quite a bit more intensive. The theory behind his therapy was that people's lives were basically "pre-scripted" by their past-life experiences. For instance, a person who was abused and made to feel worthless in one life carried that programming with them, causing them to seek out similar experiences the next time around, in order to cast—and produce—their life's "script." He said people often unconsciously repeat these patterns over several lifetimes, until they're made aware and spend the time necessary to correct them.

Since I already suspected Jack's final night aboard *Titanic* had adversely affected my psyche, I connected with what he was saying.

Another interesting point he made was that, not only does the memory of a past-life trauma leave a scar, but also a person's *mindset* at the time of his or her demise—which included things he or she may have heard at that moment. For instance, a homicide victim carried with them the memory of the things the killer said right before the murder, with the result being that this negative feedback became part of the mind's permanent programming.

Mark told me the point of the therapy was to undo this programming, which would allow me to start over with a fresh slate.

We then talked about my particular situation. I acknowledged in general terms my previous past-life regression experiences—without revealing Jack's name or association with *Titanic*. I referred to him as a "minor historical figure," since I didn't want Mark's expectations to skew the results of any subsequent regression.

However, I did tell him that, while I was certainly interested in wiping away the "programming" that was holding me back, I was also curious by nature, and given that I'd spent a great deal of time documenting my spiritual journey, I had an interest in exploring the details of Jack's life, in order to prove—at least to myself—that the connection was real.

Mark cautioned me on these expectations, saying it was unlikely that a past life could ever be "proven" as such. He said it would be better for me to focus on the healing.

"But if your goal is simply to re-experience your past lives by watching them like a movie," he said, "you can find any number of other hypnotherapists to regress you."

We talked about the process of his therapy. Mark said he allowed the client's subconscious to direct the work, since a person's subconscious was well aware of its problems.

He went on to explain the subconscious remembers everything that's ever happened to it, kind of like a tape recorder that's constantly running. Thus, it's easy to pick up where you leave off between sessions, kind of like going back to the tape. And, he said, you can go back over the same "piece of tape" many times, and it'll always stay the same. According to

Mark, stories revealed under past-life regression remained consistent.

Soon my time was up, and after paying for the session, I left. Mark told me he was going on vacation for a few weeks, and that he'd drop me an email when he returned to schedule the follow-up session.

While he was out of town, I wrestled with the decision of whether or not I wanted to work with him. On the one hand, I agreed wholeheartedly that healing was—*or at least should be*—my main objective. God knows how I wanted to lose what had certainly become, by that point, an unhealthy emotional connection/obsession with *Titanic*.

However, on the other hand, I still felt it was important to document the regressions. I understood Mark's reasons, and while I respected them, I felt I'd come so far in the project— meticulously saving notes and receipts every step of the way—to allow something as big as a full-blown hypnotic regression to take place without having a way to refer back to it later. As much as I wanted the healing, I felt equally compelled to continue documenting the process.

What Mark had said about past-life stories not changing from regression to regression also stuck in my head. Assuming this was true, and also assuming I could find another hypnotherapist who'd be amenable to taping the sessions—I figured I could always come back to him later if I still felt the need for closure.

Around this time, I also had a heart-to-heart conversation with Pat. While updating him on the status of the project, I finally got up the nerve to ask him the question I'd wanted to for a while.

"Do you believe me?"

He carefully considered his response
lieve it."

When I challenged him on this answ
wasn't making it up, but he couldn't r
thing wasn't some sort of subconscious w..
either.

I was taken aback by this.

"What?" I said. "You think I want to be Jack for the so-
called 'bragging rights?' So I can go to cocktail parties and
say 'did you know I was a famous hero in my past life?'"

"Something like that," he said.

I told him that wasn't my intention at all. And although he
knew I was working on a book, I told him I honestly didn't
know whether I wanted to publish it.

"Look," I said, "I'm writing this for *me*. I want to get the
Titanic business out of my head. If I was Jack and his tragic
life has negatively affected me—I want to fix it and get on
with my life."

I did, however, admit that, in at least one respect, I was
happy my past life appeared to be associated with *Titanic*. But
not—I pointed out—because Jack was famous. But rather,
because his life was documented. He wasn't some anonymous
person whose story I could never hope to corroborate.

"My ultimate goal," I told him, "would be to verify things
from Jack's life, so I could know that death is not the end. So
I could have tangible proof that—as they say—life goes on.
Before I die, I'd very much like to know this."

He was silent for a moment.

"You know," he said, "I think you're setting yourself up
for failure. People have been trying to prove that for thou-

us of years, and no one has, so why do you think you can?"

I told him I realized it might be a quixotic task, but I reiterated that I intended to at least try.

He didn't respond right away. However, a few weeks later, after he'd thought about it some more, he told me he still felt I was trying to "prove" not one, but *two*, impossible things: that reincarnation as a phenomenon was real and that I'd been Jack Phillips.

Since I did—and still do—respect Pat for his honesty, it was certainly depressing to realize he could be right. However, I knew I needed to soldier on with the work—wherever it took me.

But at that moment, the only thing I was sure of was that, with Mark Benton out of the picture, I was basically back to square one. (Or square two, since I still had the MP3 regression tape, which I hadn't played since that breakthrough night a couple of months earlier.)

One evening, shortly after deciding not to continue with Mark, I tried it again. But unfortunately, no new information came. I don't know if I was too tired, or else too wired by my vivid memories of the previous successful session; but, for whatever reason, the tape wasn't working for me anymore, and I needed to find someone—*or something else*—that would.

CHAPTER TWENTY-THREE

SOS

Jack, North Atlantic, April 15, 1912

Jack carefully typed out the distress call, one letter at a time.

CQD CQD CQD DE MGY MGY MGY Position 41.44 N. 50.24 W

He waited for a response, and when none immediately came, he fired off another. This time, however, he'd barely finished sending, when he got one.

What is the matter with you? asked a ship whose call sign was DFT.

Jack quickly handed the scrawled message form to Harold, then flashed back:

Sinking by the head and require assistance at all possible speed. Please tell your captain.

Ok. Standby, the ship's operator said.

ck waited, he asked Harold to look up the call sign
ip.

"It's the *Frankfurt*," the boy said, thumbing through the
Marconi manual. "Krauts," he continued, wrinkling his nose.

Jack nodded. "Best go tell the captain."

Although Jack, like most Englishmen, didn't have any
great love for "Krauts"—or Germans—when it came right
down to it, he didn't care if the ship was Chinese, so long as it
came to their aid.

What is your position? Jack asked the German ship.

When he got no immediate response, he assumed the
ship's wireless officer had gone to inform his captain of *Titanic*'s predicament.

Harold returned, saying, "He wants his position."

"Yes," Jack said, "waiting for it now."

Jack was buoyed by the fact that the ship's broadcast signal seemed loud, which meant it was relatively close. On the
other hand, he knew Germans had their own Marconi devices,
so he wasn't sure the British standard applied with them.

Jack sent the distress call again and again, and the minutes
seemed to crawl by, without a response from the German, or
any other ship.

"What's taking the Kraut so long?" Jack thought. "And
where the hell was everybody else?"

Suddenly, the headset came alive once again. Another
ship, whose signal was so faint Jack could barely hear it, was
sending him a message.

Do you know that Cape Cod is sending a batch of messages for you?

"Cape Cod?" Jack thought, "*The news service?* What?! Has everyone gone daft this evening?" He fired back: *Come at once. We have struck a berg. It's a CQD Old Man.*

Shall I tell my captain? Do you require assistance? the ship's operator asked.

"Yes, you fool," Jack thought, but was nicer about it when he replied. *Yes, at once.*

Ok. Standby, the other ship said.

As Jack handed Harold the slip of paper, the boy said. "It's the *Carpathia*. Cunard Line."

Jack nodded. "Good," he thought. "A proper British ship." Since he'd worked on Cunarders before—*Lusitania* and *Mauretania*, among them—Jack knew the ship's Marconi officer would do as promised, unlike the Kraut, who—God knows what he was up to.

Jack flashed the distress call again. The room was silent, save for the spark of his sending and the scratch of pen on paper as Harold continued transcribing the sent and received messages into the logbooks.

A few minutes later, *Carpathia* responded.

Tell your captain we've turned and are heading north to meet him.

Jack handed the form to Harold, and told him to inform Captain Smith. The boy left the room as if fired by a rocket.

What is your position? Jack flashed back.

Standby, Carpathia responded.

While Jack waited for the response, Harold returned with Captain Smith and another of the ship's officers.

Jack removed his left headphone, and told the captain *Carpathia*'s Marconi officer was getting his ship's location.

The minutes crawled by, as Jack, Harold and the grim-faced officers waited impatiently for the information.

Soon the *Carpathia* sent the coordinates, and Jack handed the paper to Captain Smith, who took a seat at Harold's desk to make some calculations. The other officer stood over his shoulder, while Harold leaned, out of the way, against the door to the Silence Cabin.

Once the captain was finished, he asked the officer to double-check his figuring. The officer nodded at the captain.

Then the old man turned to Jack. "They're fifty-six miles away. Even at top speed, it will take them four hours to get here."

Jack nodded at the captain, not sure where this was heading.

"Let's hope we find someone closer," the captain said stonily, before he and the other officer swept from the room.

Jack's eyes widened, and his stomach took a sickening plunge. Putting his headphone back on, he resumed sending the distress call—

CQD de MGY I require assistance immediately. Struck by iceberg in 41.46 N. 50.14 W

—as Harold returned to his desk, and continued updating the logbooks.

"Where's the Kraut?" Jack wondered again. He sent him a message:

Are you coming to our assistance?

What is the matter with you? the Kraut asked again.

Gritting his teeth, Jack replied: *We have struck an iceberg and sinking. Please tell captain to come.*

OK, the Kraut responded. *Will tell the bridge right away.*

"It's about time," Jack thought.

OK, yes, quick, he replied,

Where the hell was that other ship, Jack wondered. The "Chatterer?" The one who'd blasted his eardrums earlier. Hadn't he said he was stopped, *surrounded by ice?* This had to mean he was closer than four hours away.

Jack sent a message back to *Carpathia,* urging her to proceed to their location at the greatest possible speed.

While he waited for *Carpathia* to acknowledge the message, a deafening roar filled the Marconi Room. It was so loud that Jack, even with his headphones on, could hear nothing but the noise, which continued to increase in volume.

Looking through the skylight, Jack saw a huge torrent of white smoke pouring from the ship's forward funnel.

At that moment, the officer who'd been with Captain Smith earlier returned and handed Jack a piece of paper. Jack took off his headphones, and the officer yelled into his ear, "This is our updated position!"

But even with the man screaming at him from inches away, Jack could barely make out the words.

He turned to Harold: "Tell the captain I can't hear anything!"

The boy jumped up once again and rushed from the room.

The officer then did a bit of pantomiming. Reaching over Jack's desk, he took the original scrap of paper with *Titanic*'s latitudinal and longitudinal information on it, balled it up and tossed it into the trash bin beneath Jack's desk. He then took the new piece of paper Jack was holding and slammed it down firmly on his desk. Jack nodded to let the officer know he understood.

As soon as the man departed, Jack, who still couldn't hear anything, sent a message to the Cunarder, informing her of their updated position.

Then, leaning over, he once again fished the Chatterer's message from the trash, to remind himself of the ship's call sign—MWL. Memorizing it, he tossed the paper back into the bin.

He then addressed a CQD message specifically to the ship.

By this time, the intense roar had begun petering out, so Jack could hear *Carpathia* acknowledging it had received the new information.

But still, there was no answer from MWL, the ship Jack knew was closer.

Jack looked at the clock, which read 12:46 am. He suddenly had a panicked thought. What if the "Chatterer's" ship only had a single wireless officer? If that was the case, wasn't it likely the man would already be in bed?

He attempted to push this thought away, but his stomach began to ache just the same.

Harold returned moments later. "He was venting the boilers," he said.

Jack nodded, and continued sending the CQD. But still, no response from the Chatterer, or any other vessel.

"Where are all the bloody ships?" Jack thought. Then he flashed on an image that made him shiver.

He was back in Southampton, watching the adrift steamer *City of New York* narrowly avoid colliding with *Titanic*. And Jack, who'd watched the drama play out from high atop the Boat Deck, suddenly recalled that he'd seen dozens of other steamers docked along the river—all idle, due to the coal worker's strike.

In fact, as Jack later learned from Jim, the reason the *New York* had been so far out in the river was because *there hadn't been any more dock space left in the entire port.*

Jack had to assume that all of these ships were, even now, still sitting back in England, their regularly scheduled crossings cancelled on account of the strikers.

"Those bloody, Irish bastards," he thought again, as a feeling of impotent rage began building in his chest.

And although he tried not to think about it, the infuriating sight of all those docked steamers continued replaying in his mind. He even recalled seeing old *Teutonic* among them. The irony wasn't lost on him. He realized that, in all likelihood, he'd caught a glimpse of his very first steamer, from the deck of what could well end up being his last.

Once again, he cursed the selfish and cowardly coal workers for their greed.

During the next several minutes, Jack's hopes were raised and quickly dashed, as a couple other ships responded to the CQD. However, once the calculations were made, they were all found to be too far away.

At one point, Harold tapped Jack on the shoulder, signaling for him to take off the headphones.

"Maybe you should try SOS," he said. "It's the new signal."

Jack looked at him blankly. SOS? Then he remembered. The boy was right. This new distress signal had recently been adopted by the Berlin Conference. However, the CQD signal, which had been made famous by Jack Binns, was still the one most often used.

"Yeah," Jack said, "suppose so. Guess it couldn't hurt."

"Yeah, it might be your last chance to use it," Harold said.

Jack glared at him as he put his headphones back on.

After that, he alternated signals, transmitting CQD and SOS intermittently. However, the effect was still the same. No new ships answered either call.

As the minutes dragged by, Jack's feelings of impotence and helplessness began to grow, and it didn't help that he was also dying for a cigarette.

He got up from his chair, and asked Harold to spot him for a bit.

"I'm gonna go and have a look see," he told him.

Bundling up against the cold, Jack headed outside, where he noticed right away things were queer. The deck had a definite slope toward the bow.

Looking aft, he saw a large crowd of passengers, about one-third of the ship's length away, gathered around one of the lifeboats. Farther back, another boat was in the process of being lowered. Jack squinted to get a look at its occupants. From what he could see, they were mostly women. Scanning the figures huddled in the boat, Jack realized there were children among them as well. Unfortunately, though, Emily, with her distinctive blond hair, wasn't there.

Jack turned and looked at the empty lifeboat directly in front of him. It had been swung out, and like the others, was now hanging over the side of the ship, waiting to be loaded.

In order to get an unobstructed view of the water, Jack took a few steps toward the bow. He could clearly feel that he was walking downhill. He also noticed the inky black water was definitely closer than it had been before. He swallowed hard as he pulled a cigarette from his packet.

But even with his leather gloves on, his hands trembled as he lit the match off the railing. Taking a deep drag, he looked down again at the dark water.

Suddenly, a glint of white light, winking in the darkness on the horizon, caught his eye.

"What's that?" he wondered.

He leaned over the railing and, after rubbing his eyes, stared intently at the white glow. He realized it wasn't just a single light. It appeared to be a beacon with a bunch of smaller lights clustered around it.

His jaw dropped.

Is that a steamer? he wondered. And then: *Could it possibly be MWL...the Chatterer's ship?!?*

"Son of a whore-master!" he exclaimed aloud.

Then a voice called out to him, "Sparks!"

He turned and saw Captain Smith standing on the ship's wing in front of him, gesturing for him to come forward.

Ditching his smoke, Jack hurried toward the skipper.

"Does that look like a steamer to you?" the captain asked, as soon as Jack met him at the railing.

"Yes, sir," Jack replied. "Was just thinking that myself."

"Then why do you suppose she's not answering our call?"

Jack was aware that the captain was staring directly at him. But he didn't meet the old man's gaze. Instead, he continued to watch the flickering lights on the horizon.

"Don't panic," he thought. "He doesn't know anything. Stay calm."

"Well, sir," Jack said finally, "many small steamers only have one operator, so they don't maintain a 24-hour watch...."

Captain Smith sighed loudly at hearing this. "So you think the operator's sleeping?"

Jack turned to meet Smith's gaze. "Yes, sir."

"Well, I intend to rouse him," Smith said. "I've instructed the men to fire rockets."

The captain smiled at Jack, a smile that accentuated the deep crinkles around his eyes. Jack grinned back.

"Yes, that should rouse him," Captain Smith said again.

"I sure as hell hope so," Jack thought, although he merely continued smiling and nodding at the skipper.

"Have there been any other responses?"

"No, sir. Not since *Mt. Temple*."

"Well, keep me posted," Captain Smith said, and Jack knew he'd been dismissed.

He hurried back to the Marconi Room. As he passed the officers' washroom, the door opened, and there was Moody. Jack nodded at him.

"Duty calls," Jim said, with a wry smile.

"Yes, it does," Jack said, surprised to find himself smiling back at his old friend.

"How are you two holding out?" Jim asked.

"Okay," Jack said. "Just wish we had better news. One ship's coming, but she's still about three and a half hours away.

Jim nodded and sighed at the same time. Jack recognized the dazed expression on his face. He was certain he had it, too.

He then told Jim about the steamer he'd seen off the port bow, and about how the captain planned to send up rockets to rouse it.

"Let's hope it works," Jim said. "Oh, by the way, did you hear we lost two men already?"

"No," Jack said with a start, "who?"

"A couple of postmen drowned in the hold trying to retrieve the mail. At least, that's the scuttlebutt. They say it flooded before they could make it out."

Upon seeing Jack's shocked expression, Jim offered his apologies. "I'm sorry, I guess you knew them...."

"Yes," Jack said, as soon as he was able to recover. In his mind's eye, he could see "Book Man" snarling at him earlier. He wondered if he was one of the men who'd been lost.

"Well," Jack said, trying his best not to show Moody the horror he once again felt, "better get back to my post."

"Yes, me too."

Returning to the Marconi Room, Jack replaced Harold at the set. "Anything?"

Harold shook his head. "What's it like out there?" he asked.

"There's a steamer off the port bow."

"What?" said Harold incredulously.

"Yes, you can see the lights," Jack told him. "The captain plans to send up rockets to rouse it."

"Good show," said Harold, a wide grin spreading across his face.

As Jack continued transmitting the distress calls, he wished he felt the same enthusiasm Harold did. But he couldn't stop thinking about the postmen, whose bodies, even now, must be entombed in the freezing water somewhere beneath their feet.

The image this presented was so loathsome to Jack that, some minutes later, when Harold tapped him on the arm, he nearly leaped from his chair in surprise. "What?" Jack said, ripping off the headphones angrily.

Harold merely grinned, pointing upward.

Suddenly, there was the far-off boom of an exploding rocket, and Jack, looking up through the skylight, could see a cascading shower of white sparks high above the ship.

Nodding at Harold, he replaced the headphones and continued sending the distress call, as the rockets above exploded, one after the other.

Boom. Boom. Boom.

"Dear God," Jack prayed, "please let the bastard answer."

CHAPTER TWENTY-FOUR

THE DOOR OPENS

Paul, West Hollywood, California, November-December, 2004

A few days after realizing my hypnosis MP3 was no longer working, I remembered I'd previously visited and bookmarked the website of another past-life hypnotherapist who seemed promising.

Her name was Mary Elizabeth Raines, and although she lived in the Midwest, she occasionally came to Los Angeles to see clients.

Her site was very comprehensive. She described her techniques in detail, and offered simple memory recall exercises to help clients prepare for a session. I appreciated the straightforwardness of her approach, and also her sense of humor. Her web page was titled, "Past-Life Regression: Oh, Get A (Past) Life!"

A quote from the front page jumped out at me as well. *"If one believes that the soul is infinite, it is no more miraculous to be born many times than to be born only once."*

I'd never considered this before. Many devout Christians, I knew, dismissed the idea of reincarnation as fantasy; and yet, they believed utterly in the concept of an immortal soul entering—and later leaving—a human body. Mary Elizabeth had simply taken this assumption to its logical conclusion: if it can happen once, it can happen again.

While tooling around her website, I discovered that, like the North Carolina hypnotherapist, Mary Elizabeth also offered a pre-recorded regression. I went ahead and ordered her CD.

I tried out the recording the night I received it. However, since I'd already worked a long day, and Mary Elizabeth has an incredibly soothing voice, I found myself falling to sleep before the induction was even finished.

But when I tried it again a few days later, the results were utterly mind-blowing!

Mary Elizabeth's technique for accessing the past life was more low-key than the North Carolina hypnotherapist's. She simply had you imagine walking down a hallway, finding a closed door and opening it. And while this lacked the drama of, say the *Back to the Future* car, the regression itself provided all the drama I could handle.

Unlike the fragmentary images I'd seen using the other tape, entire scenes from Jack's life—complete with dialogue—came to me in vivid detail: Jack getting into a fight with a teacher at school and storming out of the classroom; Jack working at the post office on the day the acceptance letter from Marconi school arrived; and later, a family Christmas party where Jack fought with his father over a marriage—*his marriage*—that his parents had been arranging.

The information came swiftly and effortlessly—without any sort of struggle on my part. And I was struck right away that I was seeing things I hadn't known before. For instance, Jack's short online bio hadn't mentioned that he'd quit grammar school; in fact, it stated the opposite—that he'd graduated. So, it was most startling to see vivid evidence to the contrary. (Later, I was pleased to discover that the word "graduated" had been removed from his bio—replaced with a more vague reference to him having "finished his studies.")

Similarly, the biography had also stated that Jack had been engaged to Kitty at the time of his death...which also conflicted with the things I'd just seen. (I later learned that several women had come forward after the sinking claiming to have been engaged to Jack, not just Kitty, but researchers have been unable to find corroborating evidence to support *any* of their claims.)

However, for me, the oddest part was seeing "Jack" in action. Here was someone whom I'd only previously glimpsed in photographs, or during that fleeting first regression, and whom I'd thought about purely "intellectually," but who behaved much differently from how I'd imagined.

I should add that he seemed very much *unlike me*—personality-wise. He was bolder, and far more confrontational, than I'd ever dreamt of being. And yet, because I could hear his thoughts...I *got* him.

And the same was true for his family dynamic, which, in some ways, was oddly similar to mine, but in other ways, completely different.

Growing up, I myself had issues with my father, an electrical engineer who didn't like the fact that his eldest son preferred reading books to helping fix cars. However, as dad told me later, his issue wasn't that I was a bookworm; rather, that I appeared unfocused. And although there were *definitely* some conflicts between us when I was younger, everything changed when I became a teenager and announced my intentions of becoming a filmmaker. Dad was always so proud of those silly movies I made—and I can easily recall how he'd insist on screening them for anyone and everyone who came to the house.

My relationship with my mother, on the other hand, never required damage control of any kind. From my earliest days, she was my greatest supporter—and *fiercest* defender.

She often referred to herself as "a tough old bird"—the age aspect, of which, wasn't true, since she and my dad had married young. (They were 20 and 22, respectively, when they started having kids, as opposed to Jack's parents, who seemed much older.)

However, mom was right about the "tough" part. This was a woman who survived three bouts of breast cancer, and got her college degree at the age of 52 (becoming the oldest graduate in her school's history). And not to mention how she raised five kids—while simultaneously running a small business (a ceramic studio) out of the house.

Yes, mom was a plucky lady who *definitely* ruled the roost—which made her completely unlike "Jack's" mother, who, although genuine and warm, appeared to lack the courage to openly defy her husband.

So, eavesdropping on Jack, and his unfamiliar—yet familiar—family during the regression was a trippy experience, and it sent my head spinning.

I'd have ample time to digest it later, though. At that moment, while still hypnotized and regressed, there was one more aspect of Jack's life I needed to face, head-on.

Mary Elizabeth was now saying, "I want you to move to the circumstances and events surrounding your death in the lifetime you are presently experiencing."

In my mind's eye, I found myself back aboard *Titanic*.

"You may participate fully in the scene if it is comfortable to do so," Mary Elizabeth said in that patient, soothing voice. "Otherwise, remove yourself and notice everything that is going on from a safe perspective, as though you were watching a movie."

My body, which to this point had been totally relaxed, instantaneously tensed up. My stomach tied in knots.

"How do you die?" she asked.

There was a pause as the question hung in the air.

And then, despite having seen it before, I began reliving Jack's horrific final moments again.

But this time, it was more vivid and shocking than ever.

CHAPTER TWENTY-FIVE

THE BLACK WALL

Jack, North Atlantic, April 15, 1912

Eight white rockets were ultimately sent up, but there was never a response from the mystery ship, whose lights, frustratingly, continued to be visible from the Boat Deck. At one point, even the *Olympic*, *Titanic*'s sister ship, answered. Since she'd left England days after *Titanic*, she was at least 500 miles away.

Are you steering south to meet us? her Marconi operator asked.

Jack replied simply: *We're putting the women and children into boats.*

He continued sending out the distress call, occasionally giving updates to the *Carpathia*, in the hopes of urging her to go faster.

Come quick, old man, we're filling up to the boilers.

And all the while, he felt dead and empty inside.

He reserved his anger for the cowardly coal workers, who, in his mind, were responsible for the radio silence, and thus, the fact that a great many people were about to die.

"What about the Kraut?" he thought suddenly. Looking up at the clock, Jack realized he hadn't heard from the ship in almost an hour, when the officer promised to inform his captain *Titanic* was sinking and in need of help.

He fired off another message. *Are you coming to our aid?*

The Kraut's reply came back immediately: *What's the matter with you?*

"Jesus Christ!" Jack exclaimed incredulously. "You should damn well know what's the matter!"

In a rage, he shot back: *Keep out, you fool!*

As he continued sending the distress call, alternating between CQD and SOS, other things began intruding on his concentration: voices of passengers wandering the hallways of the officers' quarters. It was clear there was no order anywhere on the ship.

And even worse were the loud creaks and shuddering groans that had begun to emanate from below. It seemed as if the ship was coming apart beneath him.

A commotion from the hallway got his attention. It was the sound of wailing, growing louder. Jack turned to see a man ushering a distraught woman into the room. "Passengers," he thought, "and Irish, by the sound of them."

Jack gave Harold a stern look. *Please deal with them.* He turned his attention back to the Marconigraph, dimly aware that Harold was offering the woman his chair and a drink of water.

Between sips, the woman continued to wail.

"I'll see if I can find the captain," Jack heard the man say. "Will you be all right for a minute?"

The woman apparently nodded because, soon, the man was gone.

"Why aren't there more boats?" the woman asked, her voice trailing off in a fit of sobs. She quieted down for a moment, but then resumed her wailing, louder than before.

Jack took off his headphones and got up suddenly, startling Harold who was once again hovering behind him.

"Gonna take another look about."

Jack swept from the room, not daring to glance at the woman, who was now sobbing into her handkerchief.

In the hallway, the downward slope of the deck was even more apparent. Quickening his pace, he hurried out onto the Boat Deck.

At this point, the name was a misnomer because all of the boats had been launched. Even the one that had been hanging across from the doorway to the officers' quarters was gone. And although Jack didn't know it, Emily had left the ship just a few minutes earlier, in that particular boat. Even now, the girl could be seen, huddled in her long fur coat, as her lifeboat slowly rowed away from *Titanic*.

But Jack's attention was elsewhere. And the sight of *Titanic*'s huge bow nearly underwater...chilled him to his bones.

. . .

On the way back to the Marconi Room, Jack could see a man and woman coming toward him. Before they passed, he realized it was the same passenger who'd previously been crying. She was obviously in a better frame of mind now, but just the same, he avoided meeting her eyes.

– – –

During what turned out to be his last few minutes at the Marconigraph, Jack's mind remained elsewhere. And even when the captain came in and released him and Bride, the fact barely registered.

In addition to what he knew had been his horrifying negligence regarding the dismissal of the "Chatterer," Jack had plenty of other dark regrets vying for attention in his head.

. . .

He knew he'd messed up things pretty badly back in Farncombe.

The Christmas break had not been a banner one for the Phillips family, given the ongoing quarrel about Kitty.

While his sister Ethel made it clear whose side she was on, Elsie, to her credit, remained neutral, at least until the day of her departure, when Jack walked her back to the train station.

Before she left, she turned to him and said, "You should make your peace with Father before you leave. Promise me you'll try, Jack."

He was struck by the seriousness of her expression.

"Okay," he said. "But what if he remains obstinate?"

"That's our father, Jack," she said. "He is obstinate…*and you are a bit like him in that regard.*"

Jack nodded. He knew she was right.

"Promise me you'll try, though," she said again, as she hugged him goodbye.

"Okay," he said, "I will."

However, despite his promise to Elsie, the battle lines were still clearly drawn on the day he left.

His mother gave him a hug, and a packet of warm bread to take with him. But even so, he could tell she was unhappy.

This was doubly true of Ethel, who spent the entire morning in bed. "Well, bye," he called to her from the doorway.

"Bye," she said, without opening her eyes.

His father, on the other hand, insisted on accompanying him to the train station. They walked in stony silence for much of the way.

Once they arrived, he began to speak. "You know, Jack," he said, "your mother and I are not going to live forever. And I'd very much like for her to have grandchildren to spoil."

"I know, Father," Jack thought, "you've told me that several times now."

"She's a fine girl, Jack," he said, "She'll make you a good wife."

Jack pursed his lips. The old man just didn't get it. He wasn't opposed to marriage, for Christ's sake! Just not now...*and not with Kitty!*

On some level, Jack felt he'd spent several years trying to prove his worth to his father—but the old man never seemed satisfied. And to his mind, this harping on marriage was just another example of his father's continued, and unwanted, criticisms of his life.

His temper flared. "Look," he blurted out, a tinge of disdain in his voice, "I have no intention of leading the kind of life you lead!"

The words hit his father like a slap. The old man didn't say anything. He merely pulled off his wire-rimmed spectacles and began cleaning them with his handkerchief. As Jack stole sideways glances at his father, he realized the old man was indeed getting old. The stern face that had terrified him for much of his life was now just a gray ghost of its former self.

Jack knew his comment, while truthful, had been unfair. Nevertheless, he couldn't bring himself to apologize for it.

He turned his attention toward the track, where he could see the headlight of the approaching train. As it pulled into the station, Jack swung his duffel bag over his shoulder—and without another word, jumped aboard.

From the platform between the cars, he looked back at the old man, who stood, rooted in place, a furious expression growing on his face.

Jack took satisfaction however, when he noticed his father's shoulders appear to sloop.

Like a defeated man, Jack hoped, as he made his way inside the train car.

– – –

Several times since he'd left, Jack had considered writing his father to apologize, explaining once again his reasons for wishing to delay his nuptials.

He even started a few times, but always tore up the letters and threw them away after a few lines. A part of him continued to feel that the old man should apologize first.

"But there was no way to send a letter home now," Jack thought. "Not in the middle of the North Atlantic, with the ship's mail hold flooded, and the postmen drowned."

. . .

As his fingers worked the key, Jack had absolutely no awareness that a stoker from below decks had slipped into the Marconi Room and was attempting to lift his lifebelt. Then Harold's shouts began filtering through...and when he finally turned and saw the face of the grimy coal worker clutching the lifebelt—*his lifebelt*—Jack exploded in a volcanic rage.

"The gall of this man," he thought, as he pummeled and pummeled him, "this greedy Irish bastard, whose selfishness had caused the disaster."

Jack didn't come back to himself, truly, until the stoker had fallen, with a sickening thud, to the floor.

— — —

A few minutes later, a primal survival instinct kicked in as Jack, trussed up in his life belt and cradling his broken finger, fled the Marconi Room with Harold.

When they finally reached the hatch, Jack could see the Boat Deck in front of them was under a foot of water. The coal-black surface of the ocean stretched off into the darkness.

The moment he stepped outside, however, Jack realized they were trapped. His plan had been to head aft toward the stern, but the deck's incline was now too steep for walking—and there was literally nothing for him or Harold to hold onto for support. (Due to the placement of the lifeboats, this part of the ship had no permanent outer railing; in normal conditions, removable metal barricades were set up in front of the boats—but now both were gone.) To Jack, it looked as if their only option would be to brave the freezing water right away.

But then Harold yelled suddenly, "The roof! We can climb." Jack turned and realized that the roof of the boathouse indeed had a rail skirting the perimeter.

Harold backed up a couple of steps and made a running leap for the railing. As soon as his hands closed around it, he scrambled up the side of the boathouse, and quickly hoisted himself onto the deck above.

Summoning the last of his energy, Jack also took a two-step running leap. But he didn't reach the railing. His grasping hands closed around one of the railing's vertical support posts—and his right hand (with its now broken finger) shrieked in pain.

"I can't!" he yelled to Harold, letting go of the post with his bad hand.

In a flash, Harold leaned over and grabbed Jack's other arm. "I'll pull you up," he called to Jack, "but you've got to climb."

"No," Jack yelled, but Harold continued yanking his arm.

"Just climb!" the boy shouted back.

Because the ship was now titling to starboard, Jack's scrambling feet were able to find purchase on the boathouse wall. In a flash, he was balanced on top of the railing. But Harold, struggling to find his own footing, lost his balance and fell, and Jack tumbled with him to the deck below.

Jack threw out his hands to protect his face, and when his right index finger made contact with the decking, he howled in pain once more.

"I'm sorry," Harold yelled, quickly helping him to his feet. Jack leaned against the deck railing and cradled his aching arm.

A gruff voice called out to them, "Hey, can we get a hand over here?"

Jack and Harold turned to see a group of officers struggling to free a lifeboat from its storage space beneath the funnel. The ship's second officer, his hands full of tangled strapping material, stared grimly at them.

"Look, there's a boat!" Harold said incredulously.

Jack didn't respond. Still clinging to the railing, he turned away, focusing instead on the black water, stretching out all around them, as far as the eye could see.

"I say, we need some help over here!" the exasperated officer shouted again.

"C'mon, Jack," Harold said.

Jack shook his head slowly. "You go," he said.

Harold started to say something, but stopped when he saw Jack gesturing to his useless hand.

Their eyes met. Jack nodded, and then Harold, at last, nodded back in understanding.

The boy turned and hurried off to assist the men.

"What about the other one?" the second officer snapped.

"He hurt his hand," Harold said.

For a few moments, Jack watched Harold and the men as they tried extricating the boat, but then he slowly turned and began inching his way toward the rear of the ship.

At this point, tears began to flow.

His right hand throbbed as he clutched the railing. He found he had to apply more and more pressure to it, as the deck's angle continued increasing.

A part of him still couldn't believe any of this was happening. It'd been easier to pretend nothing was wrong back in the Marconi Room. But out on *Titanic*'s tilting deck, with his hand aching, his pant legs soaked and his leather shoes filled with cold water, there was no pretending.

Pulling himself along, he passed the frosted glass dome of the First Class staircase, which glowed with warm light. Jack knew the staircase would be empty now. Most of the remaining passengers were back in the well deck at the stern, and Jack was aiming to join them if he could.

He was stopped short, however, when he reached the railing at the end of the boathouse, just past the ship's second funnel. Looking down, he could see the Boat Deck was a good ten feet below him.

Spying a crewman's ladder on the starboard side, he made his way over to it. But with the crazy tilt of the ship, and his useless hand, he knew he wouldn't be able to descend it in the usual way.

Fuck it, he thought, as he placed his bum on top of the ladder and, cradling his injured arm, slid down to the wooden decking below, his butt making painful contact with every rung along the way.

Once he was on his feet, he shimmied himself along the Boat House wall, back to the port side of the ship. The iceberg had obviously hit on the other side, since it was clearly lower in the water, and Jack wanted to remain on the higher side, in case, God forbid, the ship rolled over.

As he stood clutching the corner wall of the Boat House, he could see the port railing, about twenty feet away.

He knew he needed to reach it somehow, but it seemed as far away as the moon.

As he considered his options, a couple of loud, booming reports from deep inside the ship caused Jack to simply lunge for it. He found himself teetering across the tilting deck like a drunken sailor. But soon he had the metal railing in his grasp.

He didn't even have time to catch his breath, however, before the ship made a sudden, sickening lurch. A loud roar filled the air, and Jack fell to his knees, still clutching the railing. Looking towards the bow, he could see the forward section rapidly disappearing into the sea.

Jack had never been on a roller coaster. He knew there was one in New York at Coney Island, but it had broken down the one time he and Jim had gone to ride it. So he'd never before experienced a sinking, free-falling sensation in his gut.

He was on sensory overload; his stomach flopped, a deafening roar pounded his eardrums, and his bleary eyes could see the churning water rising swiftly to meet him.

Instinctively, he took a deep breath, just before he went under.

The shock of immersion in the freezing water almost caused him to let go of the railing. He didn't though, because he could also feel a strong current that was now attempting to pull him backward. Opening his eyes for a moment, he saw dark-gray bubbles swirling all around him. But the salt began stinging his eyes, and he closed them again right away.

The whole time he gripped the handrail, he could feel the ship plunging steadily downward. But as soon the suction began to lessen, he let go. The buoyancy of his cork-filled vest caused him to begin to rise through the blackness. But now his lungs were close to bursting, so he began kicking, harder and harder, to reach the surface.

His lungs were on fire when he suddenly felt himself surrounded by fabric. He instinctively began clawing his way through the obstruction, until he felt the kick and touch of something alive, fighting him.

Jack didn't realize it, but he'd actually resurfaced directly beneath one of *Titanic*'s female passengers who was struggling in the water. He'd become entangled in her long undergarments and dress.

Finally, he was able to push her away and resurface. As he took a long deep breath, the woman continued splashing and screaming at him. In a flash, he realized what had happened, and was both revolted and horrified.

Turning away in shame, Jack gasped.

Although the surface of the water was now covered in mist...he could make out a large dark object just a few feet in front of him.

Craning his neck to look up, he was struck dumb.

It was a massive wall of black steel that seemed to blot out the entire sky. Gooseflesh rippled across his body—until he realized that *Titanic* must have come apart, and he was looking at its aft section, which, improbably, remained afloat.

He barely had time to catch his breath, however, before the air was filled with a fresh wave of bloodcurdling shrieks...and the wall in front of him began moving downward.

Jack knew he was in very real danger of being crushed, so he turned and swam away—as hard and as fast as he could. He was a strong swimmer. He'd learned as a child, back home in Godalming, in the River Wey. However, doing the breaststroke fully dressed, in shoes and a long clinging overcoat, was a new experience—especially now that his arms and legs had started to go numb.

Once he'd propelled himself dozens of yards from the wreck, he stopped. From behind, he could hear the deafening screams—and splashes—as people hit the water.

He looked around, trying to find the distant light of the bloody ship that had bedeviled him all evening. Perhaps, he thought, I can swim to it. But the horizon was now hazy, and he couldn't see any lights.

"Curse it all to hell," he yelled angrily, as the heartbreaking roar from behind him continued growing louder.

Finally, he broke down himself, his body wracked by involuntary sobs.

At the top of his lungs, he began screaming, "Oh God! Oh, God!"

He kept at it until he was hoarse.

Then, he stopped suddenly, realizing he shouldn't be cursing God, but rather, seeking his help.

"Give everything over to Him," a voice inside his head said, "just like you learned in Sunday school. Say *The Lord's Prayer.*"

"Our Father," Jack began at once, "who art in Heaven, hallowed be thy name...."

Almost immediately, the words had a calming effect.

"Thy Kingdom come, Thy will be done, here on Earth, as it is in Heaven...."

As Jack continued the invocation, a feeling of warmth began slowly spreading across his body,

"Give us this day, our daily bread, and forgive us our trespasses, as we forgive those who trespass against us...."

"And lead us not into Temptation, but Deliver us from Evil, Amen."

When he finished the prayer, he said it again. And again.

He could no longer feel his body. All the cold, the pain, and in fact, any physical sensation whatsoever had disappeared. He felt warm all over, as if he were lying in a gentle bath his mother had drawn for him.

His discolored lips, which had been mouthing the words to the prayer, began to slow down.

And whether it was on account of exhaustion, or else the non-stop stress he'd been under for the past several hours, the little remaining energy Jack possessed was soon leeched into the sea.

Long before the screams of the other victims began to fade, Jack's head slipped down inside his bulky life vest, as his lifeless torso bobbed on the surface of the ocean.

But the peaceful expression remained frozen on his face.

CHAPTER TWENTY-SIX

STREAM OF CONSCIOUSNESS

Paul, West Hollywood, California, 2004-2011

That was the last image I saw of Jack: his dead face floating in the water. And other than seeing him dressing/primping
in the mirror, this was the only other time I saw his face clearly.

When I first experienced the sinking during the MP3 regression, it connected the dots between the two conflicting
views of *Titanic* I'd previously seen: the traumatic plunge of
the ship's bow (which I vividly remembered from that late-
night "flashback") and the terrifying sight of the massive hull
from water level (which I'd viewed both during the regression, and earlier, in my backyard pool).

My initial confusion had come about because I'd seen
these scenes *in reverse order*, with the last one first.

"But it makes sense now," I thought, "and no wonder I freak out in the shadow of tall buildings! Who wouldn't, *after seeing something like that*?!?"

As I began writing Jack's story, I realized I wouldn't need a live hypnotherapist to get it out. Simply playing Mary Elizabeth's regression CD allowed more and more scenes from Jack's "life" to emerge.

Then, while I typed up the notes after a session, a curious thing began to happen. As I wrote, more and more information came to me, often faster than I could type. So much so that, once I'd finished, I'd read it all back and think, "wow, where did all that come from?"

But the approach did have one drawback. The information came in seemingly unrelated bits, like "needle drops" on an old vinyl record. In fact, during any one regression, I found myself jumping between multiple time periods in Jack's life. Thus, the biggest challenge of presenting a cohesive story was figuring out the proper order of things.

For instance, early on I saw Jack's shipboard experience with the hurricane. The event played out so vividly in my mind that I actually became nauseous during the regression. Unlike Jack, *I do get seasick—terribly so.*

And yet, despite the vividness of the scene, I didn't know exactly which voyage it had occurred during. I felt it was one of Jack's earliest ocean-going experiences, but I had no way of knowing which one, or which ship.

Since Jack's online biography said he'd gone to sea in August of 1906 aboard the White Star liner *Teutonic*, I did a web search and called up photos of the vessel. As soon as the images popped up, I thought, "Dang, that looks exactly like the one I saw!"

In an attempt to learn more about the stormy crossing, I put the search terms "Teutonic," "1906," and "storm" in my web browser. I got nothing, but when I dropped the word Teutonic, I discovered a website that listed all tropical storms and hurricanes of the 20th century.

Apparently, from August 25-September 12, 1906, a Category 4 hurricane—with maximum winds of 114 mph—had developed off the coast of Africa. The storm had crossed the South Atlantic to the Caribbean, and then, on September 7th, veered abruptly to the northeast in a trajectory that took it into the shipping lanes of the North Atlantic. By September 11th, the storm was south of Newfoundland, and, although weakening (it was now a Category 2 storm), it still had winds of approximately 95 mph.

The interesting part was the storm had been the biggest since the turn of the century, and was the only one of any magnitude that had occurred in the North Atlantic during the years of Jack's early shipboard experiences (1906-1908).

And since Jack had been assigned to his first sea voyage in August of 1906, and the *Teutonic* took 10 days or more to make a crossing (voyages to and from America generally took a month—including shore leave), it's possible the ship had left New York sometime around the eighth of September, which would have put it on a collision course with the hurricane at or near Newfoundland's Grand Banks. And if this turned out to have been the case, it would certainly be ironic; *Titanic* had foundered in the same general area.

However, since I didn't have access to the ship's records to confirm the dates, I knew I couldn't be 100 percent sure of my timeline. But on the other hand, I was encouraged by the fact that the only North Atlantic hurricane that occurred during the first two-and-a-half years of Jack's shipboard experiences had taken place precisely when I thought it did (i.e., during one of his earliest voyages). I felt that this in itself was remarkable, and it gave me the shot in the arm I needed to plow on with the writing.

Still though, I was often plagued with episodes of doubt, wondering what the hell I was doing. Was Pat right? Was I just a writer using skeletal research of Jack's life as a jumping-off point for my own creative imaginings?

In the end, the only way I could silence this voice was to do additional research to double-check the information I was getting. And the fact is, everything I researched appeared to check out, or at the very least, wasn't refuted[7].

For example, several times during my regressions, I'd seen Jack taking trains from his hometown directly to London. And yet, when I'd visited the area myself, I'd had to take one to a nearby town, and hire a cab to bring me to Godalming.

Once this thought cropped up in my mind, it distracted me so much I had to put down what I was writing and return to the web for further research.

Yes, I learned, a train line to Godalming *did exist* during Jack's day, and not only that, it's still in operation. (However, it's only accessible from London's Waterloo Station, rather than King's Cross, where I embarked from.)

I ended up checking out things like when chalkboard erasers were invented (1871). Also manual typewriters (1896) and modern, cartridge-fed fountain pens (1908-1910).

---

[7] My *"Titanic"* memories did occasionally conflict with Harold Bride's recollection of events; however, I didn't consider any of this a "deal-breaker." I'll go into these discrepancies in the Afterword.

I even researched the etymology of expressions like "git" and "Jesus H. Christ"—the latter, I was surprised to learn, was already considered "old" in 1850, according to Mark Twain, who apparently mentioned it in his autobiography.

Growing suspicious about the incident involving Jack and the East Village sex worker, I spent a good deal of time researching the history of prostitution in New York City. I discovered that, yes, indeed, brothels had blatantly existed in the city until 1920.

And even a relatively simple scene, like when Jack saw the completed *Titanic* for the first time, as he steamed into Belfast Harbor...offered multiple aspects for confirmation; among them, the specific location of the Harland and Wolff shipyard (where *Titanic* lay at anchor), as compared to the city docks where Jack eventually disembarked (the docks were further upriver from H&W, and on the opposite side, as I'd seen). There was also *Titanic*'s position at the time (facing upstream, away from the sea, as I vividly remembered).

Since the sequences involving "Mary"—the Irish laundress and Jack's one-time love interest—had come to me so rich in detail, I ended up taking another lengthy detour to see if I could historically validate her existence. Right away, I learned it would be pointless to request employment records from the Marconi Company (which still exists), since local arsonists torched the Clifden station where Jack and Mary had worked during the Irish War for Independence. (1922) "Boy," I thought, "wouldn't Jack have been ticked off about *that,* if he'd lived to see it..."

But anyway, shortly thereafter, I discovered census information had survived from that period. And since the village of Clifden—or Clifden Town, as it was called back in 1911—

contained only about 800 residents, it was relatively easy to comb through the records individually.

As a refresher, this is what I was looking for in Jack's "Mary": she was approximately 17 years old (in 1907); she lived with her elderly parents, whom she took care of; she was Catholic; she had an older brother who'd previously emigrated to the United States (along with some relatives); her greatest wish was to go to America herself; and finally, she was fascinated by steamships, particularly the *Lusitania*, which she'd read about—and later pumped Jack for information on.

Although I found thirteen different Marys within a two-year age range living in the area, there was only one who fit the description exactly. (I've chosen not to reveal her full name, however, out of privacy concerns for her family.) This Mary was the correct age, had the right religion (Catholic) and was far younger than either parent. (In 1911, when she was 21, her mother was at least 60, and her father, 73.)

According to the 1901 census, this Mary also had a brother who was five years older; however, by 1911, the man could not be found anywhere in census records—not just in Clifden, but in the rest of Ireland, as well. (I checked.) Wondering if he'd passed away, I found myself searching church and county death records, but also came up empty. I could only conclude that he'd left the country—just like Jack's "Mary's" brother had done. (Since his name was a common one, however, I was unable to track him further in the U.S.)

Now, this is where the story gets interesting: "Clifden Mary" actually made her first trip to America in 1910, when she was twenty years old. (Jack was still working at the Marconi Station at that time, although this was long after Mary had left, and the two were no longer on friendly terms.) The purpose of Mary's trip was listed on immigration paperwork as a visit, and her final destination city was Portland, Maine.

Five years later, she ended up returning to America, although this vacation ended up lasting a lot longer than she might have planned. (This is where the research gave me goosebumps.) She'd actually taken the *Lusitania*...arriving in New York in late April of 1915. Unbelievably, just days later, the ship, on its return voyage, was torpedoed off the Irish coast by a German U-Boat. It sank quickly, killing almost as many people as *Titanic* did (about 1,200).

In the aftermath of the disaster, World War I intensified, and transoceanic shipping was disrupted. I have no way of knowing whether "Clifden Mary" eventually found her way home, or whether she sat out the war on American soil; however, by 1924, she'd established legal residency in Maine.

On October 31, 1927, she found herself in a Boston, Massachusetts courtroom taking the oath of U.S. citizenship. Her paperwork listed her as single, with no children. Although I found evidence she was later deported, I couldn't confirm it, and have yet to learn anything else about her.

And while it's true I wasn't able to *prove* this Mary had been "Jack's" Mary, I found it gratifying to know that it *could have been*. I felt, given Clifden's remote location and miniscule population, that the odds were high that I wouldn't find any matches—so the fact that I did find one seemed significant.

However, this is just one example of how my critical mind was always trying to pick apart the things I was seeing. Therefore, the process of putting together the story was, at times, slow and frustrating, and at other times, heart stopping. At one point, I did come upon what appeared to be a dead end from a confirmation perspective.

This is what happened. Since I'd already seen many of the events in *Titanic*'s Marconi Room, I could easily call it up in my mind. I knew where the sleeping quarters were. I knew where the machinery room was. And I could see how the room was accessed from the Boat Deck.

One day, the critical part of my brain instructed me to check *Titanic*'s deck plans. Clearly, the location of the Marconi Room would be relatively easy to confirm. I couldn't argue, so I went back online and, after calling up the plans, was dismayed to discover that the room I was picturing wasn't in the right place at all. The blueprints showed the suite running parallel to the port wall of the boathouse. In fact, the main room even appeared to have a porthole to the outside deck!

In a daze, I turned off the computer. So here, at long last, was my reality check. I was wrong.

"But wait a minute," I thought, "what if the plans changed?" I knew certain discrepancies existed between *Titanic*'s blueprints and the actual ship—mostly last minute design changes—so what if the location of the Marconi Room had been one of them? "What if...."

I supposed there was still a remote possibility I was right, but I thought the odds against it were probably 1,000 to one. I realized *it simply wasn't possible that I was always right...and the rest of the experts wrong.* Despite my best efforts, I hadn't been able to prove Father Browne had misidentified the "Harold Bride" photo. Or that "Clifden Mary" was "Jack's" Mary. And now this....

Naturally, after this bombshell, I stopped writing, and for several days, remained deeply depressed. All I could think about was how much time I'd wasted on the project. But try as I might, a part of me still couldn't leave Jack, and the *Titanic* story, behind.

One night in January of 2005, I found myself again at the computer, doing a web search for "*Titanic*'s Marconi Room." I came upon a site by an American researcher named Parks Stephenson. As it turned out, it was his page I'd visited several years earlier—the one that recreated the audio from *Titanic*'s CQD/SOS transmissions. However, in the intervening years, Stephenson had added several new articles, including one that talked *specifically* about the location of the Marconi Room.

As I read, my eyes widened. The location of the Marconi Room was, in fact, one of those last-minute design changes! Apparently, while *Titanic* was being outfitted, its builders decided to move the Marconi suite inboard, in order to free up more window space for First Class cabins.

This meant the Marconi Room was right where I thought it was.

After the emotional rollercoaster of the experience, however, I tried adopting a new strategy: write Jack's story without double-checking anything. Just write.

I was mostly successful at this, although, I did find myself, at various times, double-checking things, just to be 100% sure.

The main parts of the story came flooding out, but it would take several years to commit the scenes involving *Titanic*'s transatlantic voyage to paper. This was because, in 2006, I stopped writing, and didn't pick it up again until 2011.

There were several reasons for the stoppage. First, at one point I read back what I'd written and realized the interwoven storylines weren't working. My heart sank as I got the deflating feeling that fixing them would require a great deal of additional time and effort.

But the main reason I stopped is that, once the key aspects of Jack's story were revealed to me under hypnosis—all of the mistakes he'd made, all the regrets he'd died with—I found myself, inexplicably, feeling ambivalent about both him and *Titanic*.

As I wrote in my journal in December of 2004:

"The most important thing is the positive therapeutic effect the whole experience has been having on me. The truth is, I've felt really great the last couple of days—ever since the 'big reveal' of Jack's final conversation with his father. I feel, in many ways, like a great burden has been lifted. What's really interesting is I can't explain why I feel this way. On some level, the things I've learned have made Jack's story even sadder—if that's possible!—and his lonely death all the more tragic and pathetic. But having an understanding about his life has—inexplicably—had a positive effect on mine. It's as if, the worse Jack's story gets, the better I feel. It seems totally backward!"

It appeared both Mark Benton and Janeen Weiss had been right all along: emotional healing was the point of past-life regression therapy.

Additionally, at the time I stopped writing, which was just prior to the ship's departure from Southampton, I realized I was out of gas. As a *Titanic* buff, I knew a lot must have occurred during the voyage. And only the highlights were known to me at the time: the breakdown of the Marconi apparatus, for instance, which Harold Bride had discussed in his interview with the *New York Times*, and later during the *Titanic* hearings; the near-miss involving *The City of New York*; and the well-documented events on the night of the sinking.

However, much of the rest of the story was lost to history. These three to four days of Jack's life, as *Titanic* sped unwittingly to her doom, were a blank canvas...a period of time in which, I knew, through the aid of hypnosis, I could perhaps make my own voyage of discovery.

And yet, I couldn't get excited about it. It seemed like a lot of work! And worse, it felt kind of exploitative, as if, rehashing these events—first for me, and then for subsequent readers of this book—would serve no good purpose.

This was ironic. I was the ultimate *Titanic* geek. I had a library of books about the disaster. Heck, I even had a lump of coal that had been salvaged from the wreck. And yet, something fundamental had changed. I didn't care about any of it anymore. I was over *Titanic*, in every sense of the word.

Another factor contributing to the delay was, while I was simultaneously reflecting on my newfound ambivalence and enjoying the feeling of "lightness" that had resulted from my inspection of Jack's life, work offers began rolling in.

Soon I was named Co-Executive Producer of a home renovation show.

The job of Showrunner, the person in charge of every aspect of a television program, had eluded me for years. And yet...with my *Titanic* obsession fading in the rear-view mirror, the job literally fell into my lap. I was elated, and spent the next two and a half years producing the show. It was, without a doubt, my best professional experience in Hollywood to date.

During this time, I discovered that another fundamental aspect about me had changed as well. One day while walking into my office building, I found myself looking up. The first thing I noticed was the cool architectural symmetry of the windowpanes as they stretched skyward. The second thing I noticed was how the cloudy sky was being reflected in the tinted glass. The third thing I noticed was I didn't feel a thing: no dread in the pit of the stomach, no inexplicable wooziness. My irrational fear of tall buildings had completely vanished—as if it had never been there.

The *Titanic* project remained hidden away, in a folder on my laptop, until a buddy from Texas, who'd seen some of my writing, remarked that I was in the wrong business.

"You should write a book," he said.

"Funny enough, I have written one," I told him. "Or at least, part of one."

He asked if he could read the unfinished manuscript, to which I replied, "Hell, no!"

However, he kept badgering me until I broke down and sent him the first thirteen chapters. He read everything in about two hours and called back excited to talk about it. Frankly, his eagerness to find out what "happened next" inspired me to go ahead and finish it.

The last regression I did took place in April of 2011. And although I hadn't used Mary Elizabeth's recording in six years, it had lost none of its effectiveness. I fell easily into trance, and under hypnosis, saw Jack's dealings with "Book Man," and, most surprisingly, learned about his infatuation with one of *Titanic*'s First Class passengers.

As I sat down to write the story, when I got to the part where Jim Moody brought the young woman to the Marconi

Room, I felt pretty much like a transcriber, typing up what I was seeing as it happened. And when the deadpan Jim introduced her as *Emily Ryerson*, I thought, "Oh, c'mon!"

I knew I'd heard the Ryerson name associated with *Titanic*. In the James Cameron movie, Leonardo DiCaprio's character steals a coat supposedly belonging to a *Titanic* passenger named A.L. Ryerson.

Naturally, I thought, that's an easy one to check. Was there a 16- or 17-year-old First Class Passenger named *Emily* Ryerson aboard the ship? I stopped writing and went online. As usual, at such times, I was nervous.

And despite the many impressive validations I'd received over the years, I was still frankly astonished to discover that, yes, there was a similarly aged passenger on *Titanic* by that name! And although Emily was listed as 18, I knew the discrepancy was negligible, because from what I'd seen to that point, she had looked—and acted—younger.

I should also mention that, after the regression, the (dormant) *Titanic* geek in me was certainly fascinated to learn the real reason for Jack's distraction on the night of the sinking.

Since Jack had otherwise been known to be a conscientious telegraph operator, his failure to deliver those last-minute ice warnings had vexed *Titanic* buffs for years—although, interestingly enough, I wasn't one of them. When I sat down for that final hypnosis session, I had no intention of trying to clear up the mystery, because I believed it had already been solved.

As part of my attempt to quantify the things that were currently known about Jack, I'd uncovered an article by a well-respected *Titanic* researcher and author named John Booth, who pointed out that both of Jack's undelivered messages (the *Mesaba* and "Chatter" ones) had been sent without the crucial MSG prefix, and therefore Jack, who was extremely busy and working solo, was under no "official" obligation to deliver them immediately to the bridge. My regression eventually showed me that Booth was right—although—as TV reporters liked to say—"there was a little more to the story."

For that reason, however, the entire "Emily" episode turned out to be a validation of sorts to me—since it flew in the face of the main critical argument that hypnotic past-life regression merely allowed the subconscious mind to serve up dream-like fantasies the subject *expected* to see...given that I'd been expecting nothing of the kind.

The fact is, if I had gone into that final regression with a list of hypothetical "expectations," you can bet a shipboard romance wouldn't have been on it. I mean, *come on!* In the wake of James Cameron's masterpiece, is there a self-respecting writer, anywhere, who'd *intentionally* create a fictional love story set aboard *Titanic?*

And yet, because I knew it was something I'd never consciously cook up, that's precisely why I ended up trusting the information. I realized it completed the puzzle of Jack's life, and dovetailed perfectly with what was known from the historical record.

CHAPTER TWENTY-SEVEN

THE MAN WHO SENT THE S0S

Paul, West Hollywood, California, 2011-2016

After reading an early draft of this manuscript, my long-time friend Stacey Miller asked me a question that's probably occurred to a few of you by now: "Given how painful those regressions were—especially since you had to endure the "death scene" each time—what made you keep doing it? Wasn't that a little masochistic?"

It's a good point, and, I think the answer to that question is that I wanted to—*no, I needed to*—discover the truth about Jack's life for myself. Since a lot of unflattering things have been written about him over the years (if you don't believe me, just check out his *Wikipedia* page), I felt it important to know whether or not the criticism was justified.

And for me personally, the most disturbing aspect of Jack's story—*by far*—was his attack on the stoker. Being a life-long pacifist, I'd found the incident upsetting to read about (in Walter Lord's book), repulsive to "watch" (during the regression,) and even the act of putting my version of it "on paper" felt like an out-of-body experience.

Since another human being had literally died at Jack's hands, it was not something I could easily dismiss, and it certainly begged the question: how could an otherwise ordinary person be driven to, if not murder, then manslaughter? (And it goes without saying that this wasn't an abstract, "intellectual" exercise for me. Having come to suspect that Jack and I shared the same "soul," I knew the answer to that question would have direct ramifications on my concept of self.)

Of course, one can reasonably argue that the attack was justified—after all, the guy was trying to take away Jack's only hope for survival. But still, it was difficult for me to reconcile the violent Jack with the person I thought I otherwise knew.

So, in the end, my "deep dive" into his life allowed me to finally understand Jack's motivation for the attack: he was transferring his extreme dislike for Irish males onto that scared, pathetic boy. (Although the stoker had actually been Scandinavian, Jack saw him as a stand-in for everything he hated about the men of the Emerald Isle.)

Naturally, after getting to the heart of the matter, I subsequently spent a great deal of time thinking about it, trying to process my feelings. At one point, it occurred to me that Jack's animosity toward the Irish could possibly have been fueled (at least in part) by repressed memories of his treatment during his previous life as "John McGilvery." After all, the peat farmer—who was of Scottish descent—had been teased and shunned by his Irish neighbors for decades, in fact, living virtually his entire life without friendships of any kind.

I thought it possible that part of Jack was vibing on this when he lashed out so violently at the stoker. And perhaps more importantly, as I looked beyond this attack to Jack's other interactions with the Irish, I wondered if this same subconscious "ick factor" had also played a role in Jack's decision not to court Mary, the Clifden laundress who, for lack of better candidates, was clearly the love of his life.

It's no exaggeration to say that his future would have been very different if he'd chosen to stay in Ireland to pursue that relationship—for instance, he *never* would've set foot on *Titanic*—and, to me, that's the most distressing "path not taken" aspect of his story. (I should also note that, whatever sexual issues Jack might've had, being gay—as we presently understand the term—was not an option for him. He was very much focused on the prospect of eventually finding a wife.)

But all of this brought up an interesting idea: what if, in some cases, nationalism—and by association, racism—has past-life roots?

If the tenets of reincarnation are true—and I have no doubt they are—the fact is, everyone on this planet has lived multiple lifetimes, on different continents, with different skin colors. So, for any of us to perceive another society or race as "other" doesn't really make sense.

However, given that racism and nationalism *do* exist, it means that other forces are obviously at work.

But...what if one of these "forces" is that we carry with us half-forgotten "memories" of people who've previously hurt us...people who—in many cases—don't necessarily match our current social or racial group?

It's a fascinating question, although clearly, racism will never have a blanket, "one-size-fits-all" explanation. These harmful attitudes can be sparked by any number of factors...and can certainly develop during a single lifetime. However, if someone presently has these attitudes, and are troubled by the fact that *they don't seem to fit in with the rest of their viewpoints and/or collective life experiences*, it might be beneficial for them to visit a past-life hypnotherapist to discover where these thoughts are coming from, and ultimately, to root them out.

But getting off my soapbox—and back to Jack's story for a moment—I believe it's an honest look at a real, but flawed, individual who found himself dealing with some of the most extraordinary circumstances imaginable.

Although, I will add one final thought: Sure, had Jack delivered those ice warnings to *Titanic*'s bridge, the disaster could have been averted—but *only* if the information had immediately been acted upon. And there's absolutely no guarantee it would have been.

In 1912, icebergs were a fact of life in the shipping lanes of the North Atlantic. While generally regarded as a nuisance, none had previously caused a "modern" steamship to sink. In fact, Captain Smith had already received several warnings about ice in that particular area, and yet he'd not been concerned enough to sufficiently alter his course, or to slow down, or to even man the bridge as the temperature dropped and his "unsinkable" ship barreled headlong into icy waters.

And a lot of other events conspired that night, too. *Titanic*'s lookouts, inexplicably, didn't have their binoculars. The sea was a dead calm...and there was no moon. Also, as Jack noted, the ship was far more isolated than it might otherwise have been, thanks to the striking coal workers, and, as everyone knows, there weren't enough lifeboats.

Therefore, the failure of the Marconi officers to properly address those ice warnings—and Jack's subsequent inaction upon receiving them—were only a small piece of the puzzle.

And keep in mind that, despite the many mistakes and oversights that occurred *before* the collision—even afterwards, hope of rescue remained, until the "Chatterer's" ship (aka the *SS Californian*) dashed it by not responding to the many calls—both by wireless and distress rocket—for help.

In the end, the sinking of the *Titanic* can only be described as a "cluster fuck," and it's not right—or fair—to blame Jack exclusively for it.

. . .

I never ended up traveling to England to see if I could validate any more aspects of Jack's life. At a certain point, I merely accepted the veracity of the situation, and began focusing on my own life instead. I did, however, make a journey that, looking back, served to put any unresolved feelings to rest.

In the mid-2000s, I went to Nova Scotia for a reunion of my father's extended family. It was great to finally get the chance to visit the place where both of my dad's parents had grown up. (Unfortunately, my mom was ill at the time, so she didn't make the trip.)

Knowing that several of *Titanic*'s recovered victims were buried in nearby Halifax, I planned an overnight side trip to pay my respects. Surprisingly, my dad opted to join me, and we ended up sharing a hotel room.

I didn't know what to expect on the morning we arrived at Fairview Lawn Cemetery, but we found the 121 *Titanic* graves easily enough. They'd been intentionally laid out in curved rows to replicate the shape of the ship.

All of the stones were bare, except for one, which was adorned with what at first looked like a refrigerator magnet, but was later revealed to be a promotional pin from James Cameron's *Titanic*. Looking closely at the etched granite, I discovered the reason: the buried man was *J Dawson*. The gift, apparently, had been left by a *Titanic* fan who'd confused the ship's 23-year-old coal trimmer, Joseph Dawson, with Leonardo DiCaprio's character from the movie.

Given how many tears I'd previously shed over *Titanic*, I hadn't known whether the reality of actually being there, surrounded by the ship's dead, would trigger an emotional breakdown. But it didn't happen. As I moved among the gravestones, stopping to read each name and acknowledge each life, I was struck by a profound feeling of peacefulness; it was as if the ghosts of the past had already moved on— mine included.

Back at the hotel that night, dad and I, perhaps sparked by our visit to the cemetery, found ourselves getting embroiled in a deep conversation. You know, the kind about life, death, and what it means to be happy in this world. At one point, out of the blue, he apologized for treating me badly during my preteen years. He basically admitted that he hadn't understood where I'd been coming from back then— although he acknowledged this wasn't a good excuse, especially given that he'd been the parent, and I was a child.

I was surprised, and, I suppose, delighted by his apology, and I accepted it right away. Looking back, that night became another turning point in our relationship. The "old man" and I have only grown closer since, and I can say, unequivocally, that I love my dad, I *know* he loves me, and that's a wonderful feeling.

I suppose it would be easy for someone reading this to assume it was just a coincidence that this heart-felt conversation happened after a visit to the *Titanic* graveyard…but I'd beg to differ. I've come to believe that there's no such thing as coincidence—especially as it relates to spiritual journeys.

While I drifted off to sleep that night, I was aware that a great healing had just occurred. Mark Benton's words came back to me…about how our lives are basically "pre-scripted" by past-life experiences…and how we intentionally seek out "similar experiences the next time around, in order to cast—and produce—this life's script." But the trick, Mark had said, was "to become aware of it, and take the time necessary to correct it."

I realized that my "script" had now changed, and the rest of my life was full of unlimited possibilities.

– – –

In the years since that first past-life regression, in addition to learning about Jack's experiences, I was also able to glean a bit of information about the other person I saw while under hypnosis in Janeen's office.

Although I initially felt that tracking down the luckless South Sea native would be an impossible task, thanks to a lucky break, I was eventually able to at least pinpoint the part of the world where he met his untimely end.

Since Pat and I were movie buffs, we were both excited when, back in the early 2000s, the Academy of Motion Picture Arts and Science announced a screening of the Clark Gable film, *Mutiny on the Bounty.*

The Oscar-winning classic, which neither of us had seen, chronicled a famous historical event where British sailors in the South Seas rebelled against their taskmaster of a captain. The men ended up setting their skipper adrift in a small rowboat and, after seizing control of his vessel, sailed it to a remote tropical island to begin a new life.

Although the film was shot in black-and-white, I had a weird reaction to seeing the island scenes. I noticed the place had the same overall look of the Polynesian island where, under hypnosis, I'd witnessed the native being speared in his leg as he raced back to the outrigger canoe.

When I got home from the theater, I went online and did some research. I discovered this part of the film had been shot on location in Tahiti.

Calling up color pictures of the island, I gasped. The beaches were sandy white, and the ocean the same indescribable shade of blue I vividly remembered from my regression.

Further research, however, showed that Tahitian beaches weren't shallow. On the island I'd seen, the "native" had been running for several yards into the sea, through water that was barely ankle deep. This meant Tahiti wasn't the island. However, given the matching colors of sand and surf, I figured "my" island had to be in the same general vicinity.

I continued researching, and soon discovered neighboring Bora Bora, which is completely surrounded by a coral reef that creates a shallow offshore lagoon. The photos were uncanny. The same color sand. The same color ocean. And the same ankle-deep water that extended for dozens of yards into the sea. I realized that Bora Bora could very well have been the place where my luckless native had been speared.

Additional research on the history of the island revealed that fierce, intertribal warfare had been common there. Raiders would often come from other islands, particularly when the males were away on fishing trips.

I learned that long boats (what I would call outrigger canoes) were used in these raids, which, from all accounts, were a kind of sport.

The source I read even mentioned that the men of the island would often *pretend* to leave, in order to catch other would-be-raiders in the act.

I realized this was a virtual description of the scene I had witnessed.

Perhaps "my" native's tribesmen had walked right into the island men's trap—possibly barely hitting land before the men appeared to chase them back to their boats.

And, of course, the native through whose eyes I'd experienced this hadn't been killed—he'd merely been wounded in the attack. I wondered…did they practice?…and then shuddered while reading that, yes, the indigenous people of Bora Bora indeed practiced cannibalism, which they enacted upon their enemies in a ritualistic fashion.

I was impressed. I realized that perhaps I'd been right about not wanting to delve further into what happened to him. A part of me, apparently, already knew.

However, my brief glimpse into this native's life ultimately brought me something else: insight into how this whole "past life" thing actually works.

304 · PAUL AMIRAULT

Appropriately enough, the breakthrough occurred during a reunion meal with the production team behind the old *Put to the Test* series. (As you may recall, it was while researching this show I'd undergone my first fateful past-life regression.)

On this particular evening, my friend Ruth Rivin and I, along with a couple of other producers, were having dinner with Joe McMoneagle, a cast member from the pilot episode.

Joe was a "remote viewer" who'd been trained in a super-secret CIA program dating back to the 1960s. He had the ability to "project his mind" to other places, and describe things he was seeing there with uncanny accuracy.

I say this because Joe did, in fact, pass our "test." From his hotel room in Houston, he was able to look at a photo of a woman whom he'd never met, and describe, in astonishing detail, the things the woman (who was down by the water-front) was actually seeing at that very second.

For me, the spookiest moment occurred when Joe de-scribed an enormous oil tanker that was passing the woman as it made its way down the channel.

Since both of our cameras were recording time of day, when we synchronized the tapes, we discovered that Joe, like a psychic sports announcer, had described the event *at the precise moment it occurred.*

Given Joe's amazing track record, I was happy to be invit-ed to dinner to meet him in person. I certainly respected his "talent"—if that's what it was.

As we ate, Joe made the comment that he believed time wasn't linear...*that all time existed at the same time.*

Then someone, I don't remember who, asked "Well, what about past lives then? Paul here believes he was the radio op-erator on the *Titanic*—you know, the guy who sent out the

SOS? But could there really be such a thing as *past* lives, if all time exists simultaneously?"

Embarrassed, I took a sip of water, although I was nevertheless eager to hear Joe's response.

"All time exists simultaneously," he said, "So, Paul, at the same time you're sitting here having dinner with us...a part of you is sitting in *Titanic*'s wireless room, tapping out your distress calls."

Apparently, my face went from crimson red to ghost white in an instant, and several people at the table noticed—and later commented on—the pallor.

The concept was unsettling for sure, but the more I thought about what Joe had said, the more sense it made. Looking back on the regression where I'd seen the native running for the boat, I could still recall how there'd been a weird "interactive" component to it. At the very moment I'd wondered what the native had looked like, I'd glanced down at my arm...going so far as to lift it up to get a better view.

I hadn't merely been a passive viewer of the events. My independent thought had directed what I was seeing. I had wanted to look at my arm, so I'd raised it.

Now, assuming my connection to the native was real, what *he thought* at that moment, I can't say. Here he was, frantically running for his life...and then, for no good reason, he pauses to hold up his left hand and examine it.

It had happened quickly, though, and I don't believe the distraction contributed to his inability to get away.

But still, the lesson about the two-way connection to the native, between his mind and mine, was not lost on me.

Thus, years later, while undergoing hypnosis one final time to learn about Jack's last days aboard *Titanic*, I was cognizant of the fact that I'd be forging a "real-time" connection between myself and him.

And although the regression proved to be fruitful, I was uneasy the entire time because I knew, looming at the end of it, was the horrifying death scene I'd once again be directed to experience—as I had, so many times before.

But when the moment came, I decided to change things up. Instead of letting myself "feel" the horrific sinking again, like a passive victim, I chose to take control. I skipped it all…jumping instead to the part where Jack was alone in the water.

And while seeing him exhausted and full of despair, in that freezing ocean, I sent him unconditional love.

"It's okay," I told him. "You did nothing wrong. It's okay." I repeated it like a mantra.

I'd seen the death scene, over and over, since 2004. It was always the same. I knew eventually he'd have a thought, a powerful one that would help him deal with the horror of the situation. It would be a small voice in his head—his voice—telling him to "say *The Lord's Prayer*."

The first time I'd seen it, I simply watched it all unfold like a movie. Jack repeating the prayer…and feeling the powerful surge of warmth spreading across his body, calming him, and making him feel peaceful and sleepy.

I knew that science had another explanation for the things he was experiencing. The onset of hypothermia reportedly causes a kind of hysteria in its victims, who inexplicably feel like they're hot, causing them to strip off the very clothing and blankets meant to warm them.

I had to assume this was what Jack was feeling at that moment, while his body was convulsing with shivers so violent they seemed more like spasms.

The first several times I'd witnessed the scene, I also noted the reverence with which Jack had repeated this most famous of Christian prayers. I accepted what I perceived to be his religious conviction, in the same way I accepted his relative "conservativism"; both were alien concepts to me, since I had differing spiritual and political points of view. But I certainly didn't judge him for it. On the contrary, I thought it was a blessing that—after all that pain and horror he endured—he was able to face his death with *any sort of peacefulness*.

However, between 2004 and 2011, thanks in no small part to the healing that had been brought about by learning Jack's story, I myself had undergone a radical change of thinking regarding the Divine.

This is the reason I found myself, while doing my last regression, sending Jack unconditional love as he struggled in the freezing water. I was grateful for all the gifts his life had revealed to me. He had helped me grow, and to see the world in a much different way. My weird obsession with his life had sent me on a voyage of spiritual self-discovery that had ultimately changed mine.

Thus, instead of allowing myself to feel his horror and desperation during those heartbreaking final moments, I decided to be happy, even joyful, for the experience.

And then, as I watched him screaming his lungs out as his life force ebbed away in the frigid North Atlantic, I realized, in a blinding flash, that I could actually *do something* to help him.

I could use my connection to him—whatever it was—to share the very thing he'd re-awoken in me: a deep and unflagging belief in God, the source of all Love.

"Say the Lord's Prayer," I told him at last. *"Say the Lord's Prayer...."*

I realized I'd come full circle.

EPILOGUE

Paul, West Hollywood, California, October 2016

"We sure took some amazing pictures," I thought.

As I thumbed through the photo app on my iPhone, I recalled that it had been one of those marvelous spring days in Southern California, where a recent windstorm had swept the pall of smog from the Los Angeles basin, leaving behind uncharacteristically blue skies. My partner, Jimmy, and I had been determined to get out and enjoy the scenery.

. . .

Pat (my previous partner) and I had separated in 2005; the breakup having little to do with our conflicting views on my past-life search, but rather, the dawning realization that—after almost thirteen years—we'd drifted apart and wanted different things out of life. We've remained friends, however, occasionally getting together for dinner or to watch some old but well-loved movie.

Oddly, Pat was with me four years ago when I met Jimmy at a fundraiser. I'd spotted Pat from across the crowded room, and the two of us were busy catching up, when Jimmy wandered over to say hello. And within just a couple minutes, the impish redhead had Pat and me both laughing hysterically as he attempted to explain why he no longer eats fish. (Since Jimmy's slightly off-color tale involved a great deal of pantomime, I won't attempt to describe it here.) However, looking back on that moment, I'm glad Pat had shared it with me; I couldn't help but feel it was a "passing of the torch" kind of thing.

— — —

On that particular spring day, Jimmy and I had ended up in the Mojave Desert north of town. We spent several hours doing things we both love: hiking, scrambling over boulders, and taking photos.

Looking through some of the shots Jimmy had gotten of me, I realized that, with my "relationship belly" and snow-colored beard, I looked far more like Captain Smith than I ever resembled Jack. But this wasn't a complaint.

On the contrary, I considered each and every one of those white hairs a special gift—one that Jack had never been afforded. In fact, I felt the exact same way about each day I'd lived beyond the age of 25. So many milestones in my life— love relationships; parenthood; witnessing my siblings' marriages; and "being around" for the births of eleven beloved nieces and nephews—were things that could otherwise have been missed, and I knew it. So I was grateful.

I was also grateful for Jimmy's presence in my life, and for the fact that we lived in a beautiful place where we could slip

away at a moment's notice to enjoy the splendor of nature—
and return home again in the space of an afternoon.

Looking over the last batch of photos we took that day—of
a lonely stand of Joshua Trees we encountered on the way
back—I could easily recall how that particular trip had ended.

. . .

As we piled into the truck, satiated by the much-needed
transfusion of scenery, my mind had already returned to practical matters—namely, what we were going to do about
dinner.

"So," I began, "what would you think—"

But Jimmy cut me off right away. "Pizza!" he said, sport-
ing that trademark grin.

I laughed, both because that's *exactly* what I'd been thinking, and also because I knew my "relationship belly" wouldn't
be going anywhere soon.

And I was 100 percent okay with that.

AFTERWORD

One of the enduring mysteries of the *Titanic* disaster is why the "Chatterer's" ship, MWL, the ***SS Californian,*** never came to their aid. The subject has been debated for the past hundred years, and will probably be discussed for hundreds more.

In regards to the message Jack unfortunately blew off, *Californian*'s Marconi Officer Cyril Evans testified at the U.S. *Titanic* Hearings that he'd been instructed by his captain to send a message to *Titanic*, the only ship known to be in the area, informing her that she—the *Californian*—had stopped for the night due to heavy field ice that was surrounding the ship.

Unfortunately, Evans was never asked, nor did he explain, why he hadn't followed established Marconi procedure in relaying this message. Not only did he not use the MSG prefix, which would have marked it official correspondence to the ship, he also disregarded the Marconi rule that an officer instructed to send an MSG was required to wait and receive confirmation that the message had not only been received, *but delivered and acknowledged* by the bridge on the receiving end.

Following his dismissal by Jack, Evans had merely listened to *Titanic* sending to Cape Race for several more minutes, before finally turning off his set and heading to bed, which he did at approximately 11:25 pm, twenty minutes before the collision.

When *Californian*'s crewmembers later reported to Captain Stanley Lord (coincidentally, no relation to *Titanic* historian Walter Lord) that a nearby ship was firing rockets, instead of waking up Marconi Officer Evans, the captain merely ordered his crewmembers to try and communicate with the vessel via a Morse lamp. This was done repeatedly, to no avail, *for two hours*, during which time the lights of the distant steamer were plainly visible from *Californian*'s deck.

At the time *Titanic* sank—approximately 2:20 am—members of *Californian*'s crew reported seeing the ship appear to "steam away to the south." But it wasn't until 5:30 am that Marconi Officer Evans was awakened and asked to see if he could find news about "a ship that has been firing rockets in the night."

As soon as Evans turned on his set, he learned of the disaster—and once the information filtered to the bridge—the *Californian* hurried to the site of *Titanic*'s last reported position. But by then it was much too late.

In his book *The Night Lives On*, Walter Lord pointed out that Marconi Officer Evans had only been awakened *after* the sun had risen, a fact that, to the writer's mind, wasn't coincidental. Since an abundance of caution had caused *Californian*'s skipper to stop in the first place—after discovering his ship was surrounded by large icebergs during a pitch-black night—writer Lord surmised the reason Captain Lord hadn't been more aggressive in trying to learn about—or help—a nearby ship in distress was because he knew he'd have to risk his own neck to do so.

At both the American and British Inquiry hearings, the conduct of the *Californian* was singled out for blame. According to the American report, *"Her officers and crew saw the distress signals of the Titanic and failed to respond to them in accordance with the dictates of humanity, international usage, and the requirements of law."*

"In our opinion such conduct, whether arising from indifference or gross carelessness, is most reprehensible, and places upon the commander of the Californian a grave responsibility."

"Had assistance been promptly proffered, or had the wireless operator of the Californian remained a few minutes longer at his post on Sunday evening, the ship might have had the proud distinction of rescuing the lives of the passengers and crew of the Titanic...."

The **SS Frankfurt**: Although Jack felt the German liner had also been less than helpful that evening, the reality was it was too far away to do any good. At the time of the first CQD transmission, the steamer was more than 150 miles from *Titanic*. In the end, and despite Jack's brush-off—which *Frankfurt*'s wireless officer later claimed he hadn't heard—the ship actually responded to the distress call, arriving six hours after *Carpathia*. However, upon seeing no sign of *Titanic*—or survivors—the liner resumed its voyage to Germany.

Harold Bride: After separating from Jack on the roof of the boathouse, Harold assisted crewmembers trying to free the collapsible lifeboat that was stored beneath *Titanic*'s forward funnel. He and the other officers were eventually able to extricate the boat, which they pushed onto the flooded Boat Deck below. Unfortunately, the craft landed upside down, and as Harold and the officers scrambled to right it, the huge wave caused by the sudden plunge of the bow swept them overboard. Harold ended up underwater beneath the lifeboat, before being pulled aboard. He spent much of the night on this makeshift raft, along with 27 other crewmembers, and was later rescued by the *Carpathia*.

He returned to England, but eventually left the Marconi Company. He went on to marry Lucy Downie, a schoolteacher, and settled in Scotland, where he became a salesman.

Regretfully, it also must be pointed out that, in this writer's opinion, Bride was actually the source of much of the disinformation that has circulated about Phillips over the years. In his interview with the *New York Times*, which his—and Jack's—boss, **Guglielmo Marconi** *had personally arranged, and was present for*, Harold claimed that the mood in the Marconi Room had actually been lighthearted that evening...in fact, that he and Phillips had mocked *Titanic*'s predicament, until the full scope of the danger became known.

"Phillips began to send 'C.Q.D.,'" Bride is quoted as saying. *"He flashed away at it and we joked while he did so. All of us made light of the disaster."* And then later, he added: *"We said lots of funny things to each other in the next few minutes."*

In his book, *Her Name, Titanic*, author Charles Pellegrino went further, reprinting one of these supposed "jokes" (apparently relayed to him by a Bride family member). The quip involved fixing *Titanic*'s problem by banging a hole on the opposite side of the vessel (from where the iceberg had hit), "to let the water out."

Although I'm certain nothing of the sort actually occurred—it begged the question: if it wasn't true, why had Bride said it was?

To find the answer, I delved into Bride's testimony before both the American and British *Titanic* inquiries, where—it's frankly an understatement to say—the junior wireless operator was not considered a reliable witness. He was recalled several times—during both proceedings—to clear up discrepancies in his testimony.

And for someone who'd been "sworn in"—and was therefore under oath—there were *lots of inconsistent statements*, ranging from simple things like whether or not Captain Smith had been wearing his life belt when Bride last saw him (Bride's first answer: *emphatically* "No" / Later: "I have no way of knowing"); to how much the *New York Times* had paid him for his story (Bride's first answer: "$1000" / Later: "$500"); to even whether or not there was "breathable air" in the capsized lifeboat he'd found himself stuck under (Bride's first answer: "Yes, sir." / Later: "I couldn't find any").

But the biggest problem for investigators was that Bride claimed to be unaware of *any messages* sent to *Titanic* involving the ice danger, with the sole exception of one that had come in while he himself had manned the Marconigraph (earlier that evening, before the collision, while Jack was eating dinner).

This was his testimony (from the American hearings):

Bride: I received the message myself and gave it to the captain. It stated that there were three large icebergs the ship had just passed, and it gave their position.

Oddly, during this same exchange, after stating three times that he'd delivered the message personally to Captain Smith, Bride suddenly reversed himself on that point, too:

Investigator: Did you communicate this message to the captain?

Bride: No, sir. I gave it to the officer on watch, sir.

Investigator: I just wanted to know whether you communicated it to the captain, yourself?

Bride: No, sir.

Investigator: You communicated it to the officer in charge of the watch who had charge of the ship at that time?

Bride: Yes, sir.

Investigator: Did you receive any other communications regarding icebergs?

Bride: No, sir.

The reason investigators were concerned about Bride's "recollections" was that other witnesses refuted him. A couple surviving ship's officers acknowledged having received additional warnings (their testimony was corroborated by Marconi operators from other vessels, who stated unequivocally that they'd sent them, and that *Titanic* had acknowledged receiving them), and yet, Bride, whose job it was to deliver them, claimed to be unaware of them.

Keep in mind that Harold—like any second officer—was plainly aware of the contents of messages delivered to the captain and/or the bridge, since Marconi policy explicitly forbade wasting envelopes on "free" messages such as these; paid passenger messages, on the other hand, required the use of envelopes, out of privacy concerns.

Consider Bride's testimony, while being grilled (again, at the American Hearing) about whether or not he was aware of any interference between the White Star Line and Captain Smith, regarding the latter's management of *Titanic*:

Investigator: Can you recall whether the captain of the ship received any messages on Saturday or Sunday from any White Star official regarding the movement, direction, or speed of the ship?

Bride: No, sir, he did not.

Investigator: How do you know he did not?

Bride: Because I should have delivered it. I saw the captain's messages. I was delivering them for Mr. Phillips.

And while Bride acknowledged that the ice warning he'd delivered to the bridge had also been handed over without an envelope, he later maintained, surprisingly, that Jack *might have* asked him to relay other ice warnings, but since they were in envelopes, he was unaware of their contents.

This comment, obviously, flew in the face of the earlier one, where Bride asserted intimate knowledge of Captain Smith's correspondence, all on account of his being a delivery boy.

So, why would Harold lie? I feel it was all part of a well-orchestrated (but misguided) effort to protect Jack's—as well as the Marconi Company's—reputation. Far from being an idiot (as a casual reading of his testimony might suggest), Harold Bride was actually a brilliant "spin doctor"—perhaps even a pioneer of the concept. Everything he said and did was an attempt to construct an alternative history; "Look, we had *nothing* to do with it"…"We didn't see any ice warnings"…"We didn't know anything"…"In fact, we thought it was all just big joke, until, well, you know…" "So, please, don't blame us for it.…"

For those who might consider this a leap, here's another concrete example of Bride's intentional "spinning of the facts," in order to give them a pro-Jack slant.

At the American *Titanic* hearings, Harold pretty candidly discussed Jack's blow-off of the German ship *Frankfurt*—basically describing it as it happened. However, investigators didn't find the story amusing. They argued, given how many lives were "hanging in the balance," that Jack should have taken the time to make sure the German operator *clearly understood Titanic*'s predicament, rather than simply calling him a fool and telling him to get lost.

So, in response to the criticism, Bride completely changed the facts the next time he recounted the story (at the British Inquiry). In this version, he claimed that the *Frankfurt* and the *Carpathia* had both called up *Titanic* at the same time, and the only reason Jack had told the German operator to "shut up and keep out" was because he was interfering with *Carpathia*'s signal. These stories are *significantly different*—and clear proof that Bride had intentionally lied to protect Jack.

James Moody: Jack's friend and *Titanic*'s sixth officer also didn't survive the sinking. He was last seen, before the plunge, working on the roof of the officers' quarters on the starboard side of the vessel, trying to free another collapsible lifeboat. Although the boat was finally launched, Jim didn't end up on it. His final moments remain a mystery because, like Jack, his body was never found.

Emily Borie Ryerson: Unbeknownst to Jack, there were actually two Emily Ryersons aboard *Titanic*. The girl whom Jack was smitten with had been traveling with her family.

The entire Ryerson clan—including both Emilys, father Arthur (a steel tycoon), older sister Suzette and younger brother John—were returning to America after cutting short a family vacation in Europe. The family's oldest son, Arthur Jr., had been killed in an automobile accident, and the family was hurrying home for his funeral. During much of the voyage, Mrs. Ryerson was reportedly so distraught she refused to leave her stateroom.

With the exception of father Arthur, the family escaped in one of *Titanic*'s last lifeboats. According to Mrs. Ryerson's testimony at the *Titanic* hearings, her youngest daughter had been taking so long to dress that evening that the elder Emily finally became frustrated and made her put on a fur coat over her nightgown. This, plus a life belt, was all Emily was wearing when she left the ship. Eventually, though, the young woman was forced to take an oar and help row the lifeboat away from the sinking *Titanic*.

After the Ryersons arrived in New York, the family had the misfortune of having to attend two funerals—one expected, the other not.

Two years after the disaster, Emily married George Hyde Clarke, a Harvard graduate and scion of a wealthy landowning family in upstate New York. The couple eventually had seven children. The ancestral mansion they lived in, Hyde Hall, still exists. It's now a National Historic Landmark open for tours, daily, from May to October.

The couple divorced in 1929. Emily later married S. Beach Cooke, an artist and writer, and lived out the rest of her years in New York, dividing her time between her home in Cooperstown and an apartment on Park Avenue.

Emily reportedly never spoke to her children—or anyone else—about her experiences aboard *Titanic*. In the 1950s, when *A Night to Remember* brought the story back to the national consciousness, she was asked about it. "I don't remember anything," she said, "and I don't want to remember." She died in 1960, of a brain hemorrhage, at the age of 66.

Ethel Phillips: Jack's older sister finally succumbed to her illness in 1922, ten years after Jack's death. She was 47 years old. Ethel was buried in the family cemetery in Godalming.

Ann Phillips: Jack's mother remained heartbroken following the death of her son, and later, daughter. She passed away three years after Ethel, at the age of 82.

Colonel George Phillips: Jack's father remained a widower following the death of his wife. He died in 1928.

Elsie Phillips: The only of Jack's siblings to survive into old age, Elsie remained a schoolteacher until her retirement in the 1940s. She never married, and died in 1953, at the age of 79.

Two years to the day after the sinking, the town of Godalming honored Jack's memory with the opening of the **Jack Phillips Memorial Gardens and Cloister,** which remains the largest memorial to a single victim of the *Titanic* disaster. Harold Bride, who'd donated a pound and a half to help fund the memorial, came to the opening, as did Kitty Bex and her family. Not surprisingly, newspaper reports at the time referred to Kitty as Jack's fiancé.

Although Jack's body was never found, his family nevertheless erected a **gravestone** at (what is today called) Nightingale Cemetery to honor his memory. Curiously—but perhaps not so curiously—they chose a headstone shaped like an iceberg.

A better tribute to Jack's life exists, albeit at the bottom of the Atlantic.

In 2001, with the aid of undersea robotic technology, *Titanic*'s **Marconi Suite** was examined in great detail by James Cameron and his team for the filming of the IMAX movie *Ghosts of the Abyss*. Very little remains inside the main room or adjoining bunkroom. The walls are gone, apparently flattened during the ship's plunge to the bottom. A thick layer of sand covers what used to be the floor.

The Silent Room (or, as Jack called it, "The Silence Cabin") has fared better. Although the thick walls have disintegrated, many of the room's contents have survived to the present day, including both the motor and transformer, which created the electrical spark Jack used to send the distress call that helped save the lives of 705 people.

Cameron's team didn't get a chance to closely inspect the equipment that had failed two nights before the disaster, but it's likely the electrical tape Jack had used to patch the shorted-out lead wires is still there.

ACKNOWLEDGMENTS

This book would not have been possible without the help of Janeen Weiss, who started me on this journey; Pat McFadden, who accompanied—*and supported*—me for much of the way; and Daryl Rowell and Mary Elizabeth Raines, who made certain I finished it.

I'd also like to thank the unparalleled Stacey J. Miller, whose enthusiasm for the project never wavered, and who literally took me by the hand to help navigate the exciting but unfamiliar waters of book publishing.

Thanks also to Shealyn Thomson, who brought my rough idea for cover art to life in a masterful way; and Sharon Pickrel, who did a spectacular job of proofreading.

I'm indebted to my friend, Jon Teboe, for his phenomenal work editing the book trailer; Gordon Fales and Karina Halim, for their breathtaking animation; and Sam Kauffman, for the terrific sound mix that brought everything together.

I'm grateful for the help of Laura Emerald, Christine Bride, Ruth Rivin, Nancy Swaim, Jenna Wims, Brad Metzger, Tim Durbin, and Jan Kimbrough, who took time out from their busy lives to give me feedback on the emerging manuscript; Rob Jacobs, for his on-going support; Kim Maria Kramer, who bailed me out after a debilitating computer issue; my aunt, Donna Mullen Good, who assisted me in fact-checking family lore; my father, Paul B. Amirault, who taught me that happiness always begins with Number 1; my late godparents, Marcia Iannelli and Donald J. Amirault, who were always there for me; my siblings, Patty, Michael, Laura and Chris, who've supported me in ways too numerous to mention; and Ruth O'Connor, who spread light far and wide before hers was so prematurely snuffed out.

Professionally, I also need to thank the late Bill Paolantonio, who was a man I'm proud to call a mentor; Lisa Bourgoujian, who taught me the importance of economical word choice and the rhythm of language; and Eric Schotz, whose passion for quality storytelling in television became infectious. Also, my high school English teachers Christopher Servant and the late Sister Mary Enda Costello, who first encouraged me to put pen to paper; and Stephen King, whose *On Writing: A Memoir of the Craft* I consider my literary bible.

I'd be remiss if I also didn't mention Father Francis Browne, "the father of photo journalism," who left behind all those indelible images of *Titanic*'s brief life; Walter Lord, who rescued the story from the dustbin of history; and author Don Lynch, artist Ken Marschall and filmmaker James Cameron, who made sure it will be remembered for eons to come.

I'd also like to thank Jemma Hyder from the UK, whose early web biography of Jack (sadly, off-line now) showed me I was moving in the right direction; and John Booth and Parks Stephenson, whose exhaustive research and superb writings about *Titanic*'s wireless officers have set a high bar.

And finally, I must thank my muses: Karyn Thompson, Mary Iannicheri, and LiLi Sorum, whose support and love I treasure; and James Young, whose zest for life and passion for art and music inspires me every day.

RESOURCES

Shortly before publication, I was able to track down **Janeen Weiss**.

In addition to being a stellar copy editor (thanks, Janeen, for your many insightful notes on this book!), she still does past-life regressions and other forms of hypnosis work. She can be reached at **janeen27weiss@gmail.com.**

For those interested in doing past-life regressions in the privacy of their own home, I can't recommend teacher and author **Mary Elizabeth Raines** highly enough. Her seminal book, *The Laughing Cherub Guide to Past-Life Regression: A Handbook for Real People*, can be purchased on Amazon. The regression CD I used, called *Journey into Your Deep Past*, can be found at the link below, along with several other recordings.

http://www.cdbaby.com/Artist/MaryElizabethRaines

ABOUT THE AUTHOR

Paul Amirault is a television producer, writer, and photographer. During the first twenty-eight years of his career, he has produced, written, or developed more than a hundred hours of TV programming for broadcast and cable networks like ABC, NBC, CBS, the History Channel, A&E, TLC, Lifetime, Bio, and Investigation Discovery. His credits include *Murder Book, Deadly Wives, The Amazing Race, Kids Say the Darndest Things, Behind Closed Doors with Joan Lunden,* and the long-running HGTV home renovation series, *Over Your Head,* among many others.

In 2007, development work on a TV program took Paul to Delphi University in the Great Smoky Mountains near McCaysville, GA. There he discovered a gift for energy healing, and he has since been infusing that passion into his work-a-day world.

He's currently writing his second book in this series, *The Man Who Was Adrift at Sea*, which chronicles his journey through the world of spiritual healing. He already has plans in the works for a third title, too.

He lives in West Hollywood, California with his partner, James Young.

For more information visit www.paulamirault.com.

To see samples of Paul's photography, visit his Instagram page at http://instagram.com/paulamirault.

Made in the USA
Columbia, SC
03 November 2020